Steamboati

A selection of art

Funne

the journal of

The Steam Boat Association of Great Britain

covering construction, operation, maintenance and navigation, published to mark the 21st anniversary of the Association in 1992

Selected by Trefor Milns, edited by Sam Wilkinson

Contributions by:-

Brian Butterworth
Peter Bridge
Roger Calvert
David Carrick
Ian Ford
Peter Frost
DW Hadfield
WC MacGibbon
Janet Mills
Pat Wieland
John Winn
Joyce Wilkinson
Sam Wilkinson

Calvert Technical Press

in association with

The Steam Boat Association of Great Britain

CALVERT TECHNICAL PRESS

[illegible]

THE STEAM BOAT ASSOCIATION OF GREAT BRITAIN

First published 1994
Reprinted 1996, 2002

ISBN 0 9513620 4 6

Printed in England by
Hobbs the Printers Ltd, Totton, Hampshire SO40 3WX

Cover photograph by Marguerite Calvert

CONTENTS:

		Original Funnel Number	*Page*
1	Anchor, Rigging	60	3
2	Bearings, Split Bushes	53	4
3	Bilge Keels	60	5
4	Boiler Designs	45	6
5	Boiler Operation	12	16
6	Brass & Bronze Polishing	55	23
7	Burners, Oil	61	24
8	Check List	38	28
9	Coal	49	30
10	Condensers	61	35
11	Compounding	62	37
12	Copper Pipe Precautions	46	39
13	Coppersmithing	56	40
14	Drilling Thin Metal	56	42
15	Ejectors	52	43
16	Engines	44	45
17	Emulsion on Hot Metal	51	51
18	Flag Etiquette	58	52
19	Gauge, Water Level	54	54
20	Gauge Glass Replacement	51	56
21	GRP	48	57
22	Hooks, Mooring	55	58
23	Hotwell Oil Separator	41	59
24	Hulls	43	61
25	Immersion Heater, Steam	55	67
26	Injectors	56	68
27	Installation	46	70
28	Lagging	59	74
29	Lathe Turning Tips	56	75
30	Laying Up your Boiler	20	76
31	Oilfired: Well Versed Practice	32	78
32	Passengers, What to Expect	51	79
33	Pressure Gauge	53	82
34	Propane Firing	19	83
35	Propane Precautions	48	87

36	Propulsion	44	91
37	Propeller Maintenance	59	95
38	Pumps	60	97
39	Reamers	50	99
40	Safety I	48	100
41	Safety II	31	102
42	Safety III	52	108
43	Safety at Sea	54	110
44	Safety Valve	51	111
45	Seamanship I	58	113
46	Seamanship II	50	118
47	Silver Solder	49,60	123
48	Slide Valve	55	125
49	Slipways	43	127
50	Spanish Windlass	48	130
51	Stainless Steel - Beware	49	131
52	Steering Cables	49	132
53	Stud Driving	56	133
54	Taps	49,53	134
55	Thrust Block	58	135
56	Trailers I: Rules	52	137
57	Trailers II: Maintenance	59,60	141
58	Trailers III: Stability	49	143
59	Tube Bending	53	144
60	Twist Drill Sharpening	50,51	149
61	Valve Gear	57	150
62	Valve Setting I	77	152
63	Valve Setting II	48,56	155
64	Varnishing	48,53	156
65	Water Treatment	37	157
66	Whistles and Sirens	59	162
67	Winch Line	49	164
68	Woodscrews, Lubrication	48	165
	Index		167

Note on Figures: For technical reasons, it has not always been possible to reproduce the original figures from the FUNNEL articles. In such cases, diagrams have been re-drawn and equivalent photographs used.

1. **RIGGING AN ANCHOR**

When rigging any type of anchor it is essential to have a length of chain attached to its stock before changing to rope. Between 6 and 12 feet will be required depending on the size of your boat. You will have to use your own judgement on the size of chain but err on the large side. Its function is to hold the anchor stock down on the sea bed. To facilitate this you must pay out at least three times as much warp as the greatest depth of water that you are mooring in.

2. SPLIT BEARING BUSHES

The best way to produce accurate split bushes is: Rough machine the bush, leaving an ⅛" finishing allowance all over. Carefully mark the position of the split along the sides and across the ends. Cut in half with a hacksaw, cutting along the lines from both sides to the centre. Now set up sideways in a four jaw chuck and skim to clean up both butts. Tin the butts with soft solder, wiping off any surplus. Gently clamp the two halves together in a vice, lining up the two butts accurately. Heat with a blowlamp until the solder melts and then test with a touch of solder on the OD. Gently tighten the vice to squeeze out any surplus solder and allow to cool. The bush can now be machine finished to tolerance, keeping the line of its split on the centre line. It can then be split by gently heating with a blow lamp and while hot, wiping away any remaining solder with a screwed up newspaper. Remember, when machining, to ensure that the joint is in line with one of the chuck jaws.

3. **BILGE KEELS**

When fitting out a new hull ensure that bilge keels are fitted because they have a great deal to offer as will be seen from the following list.

(a) They will increase the stability of a boat in a seaway and when passengers are boarding.

(b) They will protect the bottom of a boat and its chines when taking the bottom and the slip.

(c) They will stop the hull heeling over badly when drying-out.

(d) They will spread the thrust of the trailer rollers or mounting pads, eliminating the risk of damage to the boat on rough roads.

(e) They provide a better location for a bilge condenser out of the mud and in smaller boats, are easily reached from inside the boat for cleaning.

The correct design is essential, not less than four inches deep and one inch thick. The bottom edge should be slightly above the bottom of the keel and protected with a strip of corrosion resistant metal. They must run dead parallel to the keel allowing for the curve of the hull, fitted at right-angles to its surface. If you already have a boat it is easy to fit wooden bilge keels. Shape them to the hull streamlined at each end together with two pieces of wood to fit inside the hull adjacent to them. Drill through them and the hull, in position. Bed both pieces of wood onto the hull with epoxy adhesive and bolt in place with stainless coach-bolts before the epoxy sets. Then fit the protective metal strips bedding them on a sealing compound after making sure that the boltheads are flush with the surface of the wood beneath them.

4. **BOILER DESIGNS**

General

Boilers are safe - if they are designed, maintained and operated properly. Folk memories of boilers exploding all over the place date from the days when engineering knowledge and materials were less advanced and before insurance companies and licensing authorities took things in hand. There is no need to be frightened of boilers, but like all engineering equipment, they need to be treated with due respect.

A few comparisons: a typical steamboat boiler might have a capacity of about 6 gallons of water at a pressure of 100 pounds per square inch (psi) and a temperature of about 170°C. The amount of energy stored in it (compared with cold water) is about 12, 000 British Thermal Units - about the same as in a small disposable Camping Gaz cartridge. If it were all changed to dry steam (see below for what that means), it would be about 65, 000 BTU (less than half a gallon of petrol). Ordinary domestic water taps produce a pressure of 20 - 25 psi (I have just flooded the kitchen while measuring this), the Gaz cartridge is at about the same pressure, while a large power station uses 1, 500 tonnes/hour of steam at about 2400 psi and 540°C.

The boiler's job is to convert the chemical energy of the fuel into steam pressure and heat, which can then be converted to mechanical work by the engine. The boiler has two sides: the firebox releases the energy of the fuel as heat, and the steam side absorbs the heat into the water. They are separated by a solid wall (usually of steel or copper) which must transmit the heat while withstanding the pressure and temperature.

Types of Boiler

There are two main types of boiler, with innumerable sub-divisions. The *water level boiler* contains a roughly constant amount of continuously heated water. Steam is drawn off and cold water fed in as required; it has a large enough capacity to cope with sudden changes in demand. This contrasts with the *monotube boiler* which has almost no capacity. The steam and water flows must balance accurately, and the heat source must change with them. It consists of a single length of heated tubing with water being pumped in at one end and steam being drawn off at the other.

Types known as *Shell*, *Water Tube*, *Fire Tube*, *Locomotive* or any geographical name are water level boilers. *Flash* boilers are monotube boilers where the water is pumped into the hot, dry tube as required, to be instantly flashed into steam. Most, though not all, steamboats use water level boilers. Flash boilers were widely used in steam cars. Modern monotube boilers (under the name of *steam generators*) are widely used in industry. There are splendid articles by George Watkins on all the different types of boiler in FUNNELs 10 and 13.

The two extremes of water level boilers are *drum boilers* (a large tank with a fire underneath) and *multi-tube* (two or three small tanks - the steam and mud drums - with a large number of water tubes passing through the firebox connecting them); an excellent example of the former is the Australian launch **FIREFLY** (FUNNEL 41, pp 172-173). Some boilers have one or more fire tubes passing through the water space to take the flue gases from the firebox to the chimney. All possible intermediate combinations can and have been used. Boilers are described as vertical or horizontal according to the direction of flow of the flue gases on leaving the firebox.

How do you choose (or assess) a boiler type for your boat? here are a few subjective pros and cons of various types:

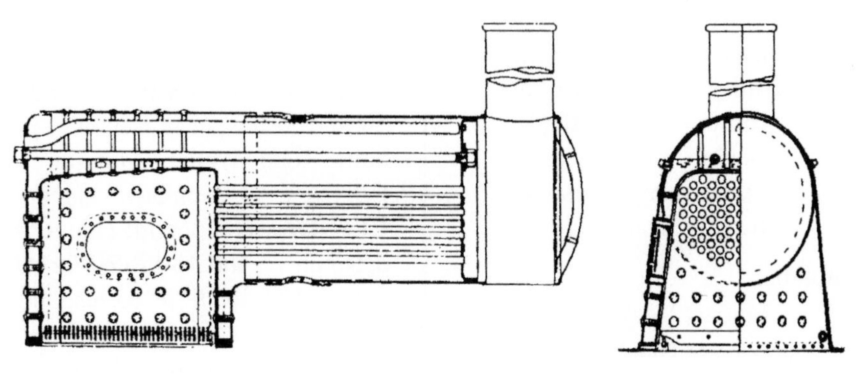

Locomotive Boiler

Vertical:

Good natural chimney draught; attractive shape for showing off a wood casing; short fore-and-aft, fairly readily available (particularly the Merryweather); flexible in meeting steam demand. High centre of gravity, slow initial steaming.

Horizontal fire-tube:

Low centre of gravity; flexible; familiar to inspectors (widely used in traction engines and by model engineers); long fore-and-aft; fire tubes tend to need frequent cleaning and occasional replacement; slow initial steaming.

Water-tube:

Compact; low centre of gravity; flexible; fairly easily made, thus readily available new; fairly fast steaming; poor natural draught; not very easy to inspect or repair; not very attractive shape.

Monotube:

Compact; easy to make; very fast steaming; inherently safe; difficult to control; not suited to solid fuel; inflexible; difficult to supply steam to auxiliaries (e.g. whistle).

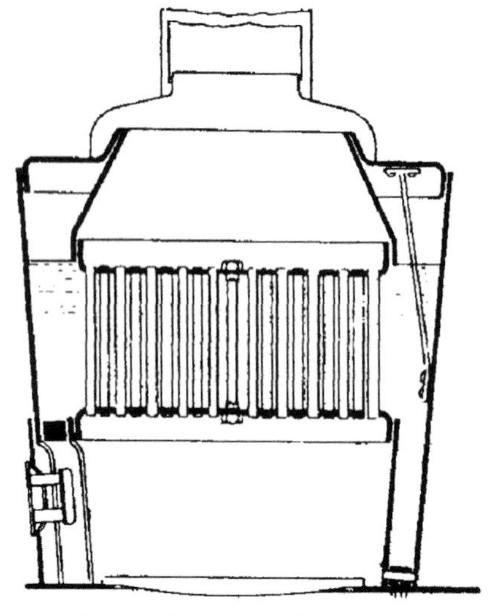

Vertical Fire Tube Boiler

How big a boiler? The main customer for steam is the engine, and big engines need more steam than small. Looking through back numbers of FUNNEL and the Stuart Turner catalogue, I find steam consumption figures around 50 to 100 lbs per horsepower per hour. Robin Wallace-Sims in FUNNEL 44 calculates values for **ELIDIR**'s (compound) engine of between 25 and 180 lb/HP/hr. (A value of 50 lb/HP/hr corresponds to an engine efficiency of about 4.5%. The maximum efficiency theoretically possible, about 35%, is equivalent to about 6 lb/HP/hr.) It is reasonable to suppose that compounding, condensing and higher pressure working would act to reduce consumption. Typical values are 60 to 70 lb/HP/hr, which would seem to be a good starting point. The size of boiler to produce a given amount of steam depends on its type and how it is to be used. All boilers will produce more steam with a roaring fire blown by a fan or a steam jet, but may be more efficient (use less fuel for a given amount of steam) if operated more calmly.

Boilers are often rated in square feet (or inches or metres) of heating surface, but this is only half the story. Most of the heat is transferred from the fire by *radiation* and thus can only heat the part of the surface which can 'see' the fire. This means that tubes behind others or fire tubes containing fully burnt gases do not do their full share of work. Only a small proportion of heating is by *convection*; measurements have shown that a locomotive fire-box accounting for one tenth of the total heating area may be responsible for half the evaporation. The range of figures seems to be about 5 - 15 lb/ft^2/hr, with coil and multitube boilers at the top end, drums at the bottom. But since boiler makers will always quote their output in lb/hr you need only consider the heating area to estimate the rating of an undocumented boiler.

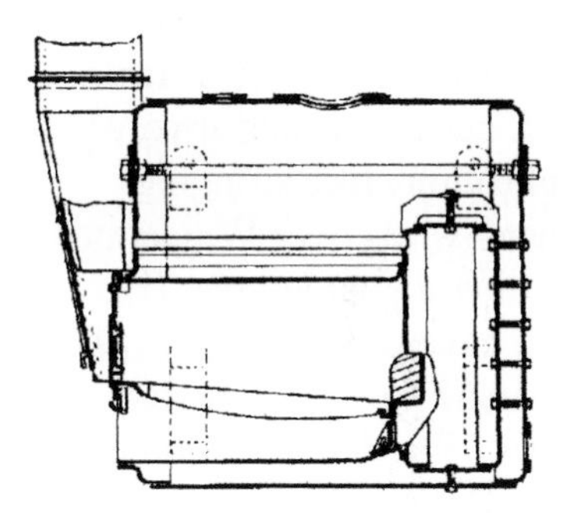

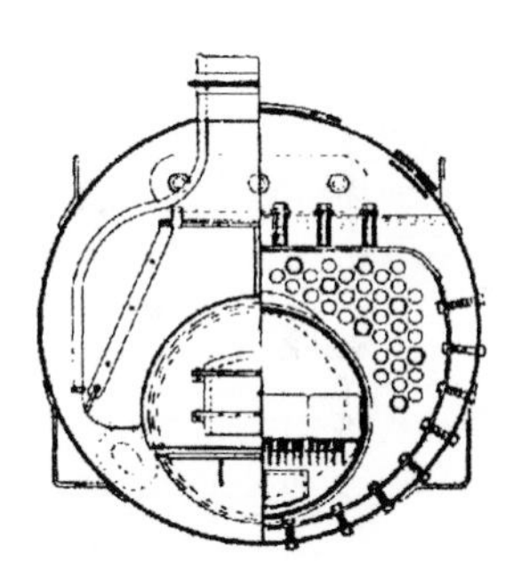

Scotch Boiler

What fuel do you use? There are lots of options; in steam boats some are more practical than others. Small nuclear reactors are unproven in ordinary use. A lithium/sulphur hexafluoride mixture has the great advantage that the combustion products are smaller than the fuel, so you don't need a funnel; however the restricted life of a boiler with this fuel (about ten minutes) makes it less suitable for boats than it is for torpedoes. Industrial steam generators are often electrically heated, but this would involve complications like stringing overhead wires over Windermere and fitting a pantograph. The French have experimented with using solar power for power stations - fine for fair-weather sailors. But on balance, the more traditional fuels really do seem to have some practical advantages.

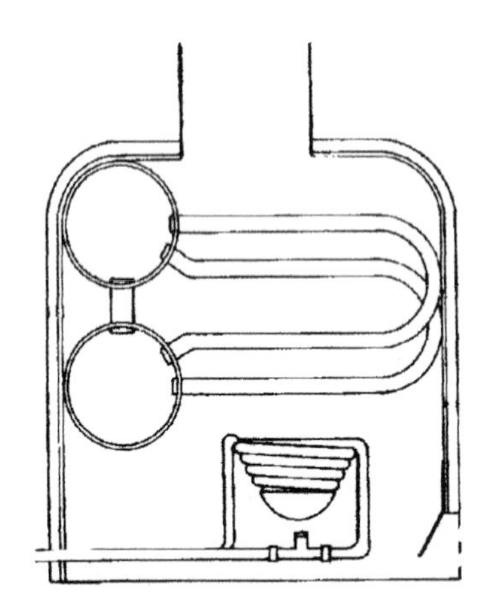

Two-drum Water Tube Boiler

(shown with a Lune valley vapourising oil burner)

Four fuels are in common use - wood, coal (and similar fuels), oil and gas. All have their advocates, although not as many wax so lyrical as Scott Pereira on propane in FUNNEL 42! A few pros and cons:

Wood:

> *Pro*: Free, clean, smells nice, produces good draught, keeps one crew member more or less permanently busy, provides a good conversation point with people who cannot understand why you do it.
> *Con*: Bulky, must be collected, dried, sawn up and stored, keeps one crew member more or less permanently busy, needs a large firebox.

Coal:

> *Pro*: Compact, stable, long-burning, traditional, will make good black smoke for ignorant TV crews.
> *Con*: Dirty, may be difficult to obtain the right grade: soft grades can give problems with soot, tar and smoke and hard grades (anthracite or coke) can

overheat the firebars, ash and clinker must be disposed of.

Oil:

Pro: Easily obtained and handled, reasonably good control of flame, compact installation.
Con: Tends to smell unless burner is very well adjusted (particularly cheaper grades), burner can be noisy, usually needs extra fuel tank pressurizing equipment.

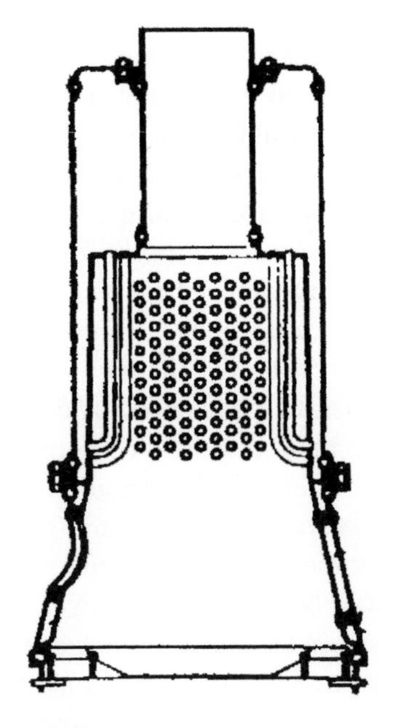

Merryweather (Cross-tube) Boiler

Gas:

Pro: Clean and silent, compact, highly controllable.
Con: Not easy to handle in bulk, leaks into bilge can lead to explosion hazard, control valves can freeze, fairly expensive.

You pays your money (except for wood) and takes your choice.

The Air Supply

No fuel will burn without air. This comes into the firebox through the grate in the case of solid fuel, or from behind the burner in the case of oil or gas. The amount of air must be carefully regulated - too little and the fire may go out, too much and you lose efficiency and may get too big a fire. While oil and gas are controlled by adjusting the fuel, solid fuel fires must be controlled by adjusting the air.

The two ways of controlling the air are by the damper and by the draught. The damper is a shutter across the main air entry (usually the ash pan) or occasionally somewhere in the flue. The draught is the flow of gases up the flue due either to natural convection or some form of blower. Natural convection is self-sustaining since

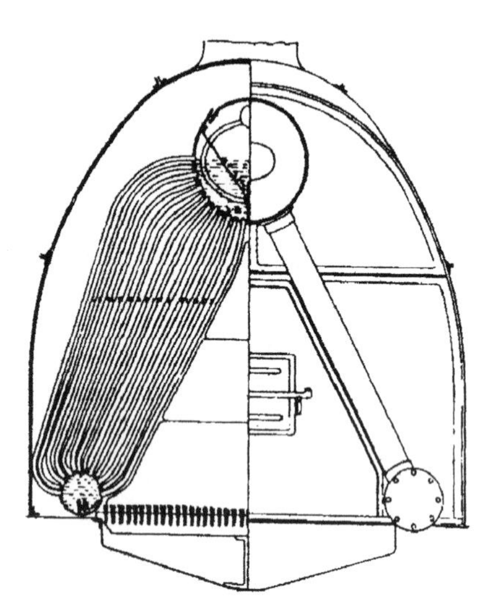

Three-drum Water Tube Boiler

the extra draught increases the rate of burning and thus the amount of convection. Although this is important, particularly in vertical boilers, it is usually not adequate for all occasions and a blower of some sort is needed. Three types of blower are common - a fan (which needs either an electric or steam drive), a steam jet in the flue (which uses steam and can be noisy) and a blast pipe (which uses the exhaust steam). The last is elegant, since the more steam you use the more draught you get. But it does rule out the possibility of using a condenser and ones passengers may get covered in sooty fall-out.

Wet Steam, Dry Steam and Superheat

Having mentioned a condenser, this seems a good moment to talk about steam conditions. Steam leaving the boiler is a mixture of water vapour (almost a gas) and water droplets at the same pressure and temperature. The proportion of vapour is called the *dryness fraction*. If it is zero, we have hot water; less than 1 is *wet steam* and 1 is *dry (saturated) steam*. The water element is no use for driving the engine (although it may be very useful in lubricating the cylinder), so we want steam as near as possible to dry conditions. A steam separator (essentially a settling chamber) will get rid of much of the water, but to remove the last bit we need a dryer, which is a length of tubing taking the steam through the flue or combustion space and thus adding a little more heat. If we continue to heat it after it is dry we get *superheated* steam. Because of its higher temperature this will produce more power than wet or dry saturated steam at the same pressure. Some degree of superheat is definitely an advantage from the point of view of efficiency, but can give problems with materials and lubrication and leads to extra complexity (a thermometer may be needed as well as a pressure gauge).

Feeding the Boiler

To put water into the boiler, you need at least two pumps (as well as the air pump). These are called *feed pumps*, and you need two because one of them is usually not working properly for some reason. In fact many people use three, one being a hand-operated pump which is always available whether the boiler is hot or cold. A boiler in steam must never be allowed to run short of water. The principal feed pump is driven by the engine and thus delivers water at a rate related to the consumption of steam. The third is steam operated and is useful for using excess steam and preventing the safety valve from blowing off in locks. There are two basic types of steam operated pumps: auxiliary engine driven (either direct acting or rotary) and injectors. (See Ron Thorougood's article in FUNNEL 38 for a description of a direct acting pump.) The injector is a very clever device with no moving parts. It works by magic and breaks all the known Laws of Thermodynamics (and several unknown ones). Unless it is made at the right phase of the moon with suitable incantations from Machinery's Handbook, it will not work at all. But when it does it is wonderful indeed. You either swear by them or at them (see FUNNEL 42).

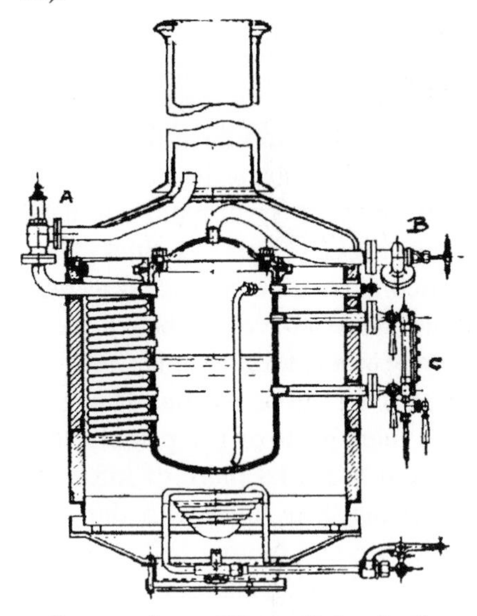

Centre-drum Water Tube Boiler (Oil fired)

Check, Clack or Non-return Valves

To keep the water in the boiler you need a non-return valve (otherwise known as a *check* or *clack* valve) between the boiler and the feed pump(s). This should be as near to the boiler as possible in case maintenance of the feed system is necessary when the boiler is 'in steam'. Similarly, the valve on the main engine steam take off pipe, the *stop valve* must be as close to the boiler as possible; this need not stop you fitting a throttle valve or *regulator* at a more convenient place between the stop valve and the engine.

Gauges

To make sure you have the right amount of water in the boiler (if it is of the water level type) you need a *gauge glass*. This is a thick-walled glass tube connected to the boiler drum above and below the normal water level. It must be protected from accidental damage by a thick glass or perspex shield. Since it is a vital piece of safety equipment it is fitted with shut-off cocks top and bottom and with a drain cock. This enables a check to be made to see that all the passages are clear.

To monitor the steam pressure you will have a pressure gauge fitted directly into the boiler and checked for accuracy by the boiler inspector. It is useful to have a red line painted on the gauge at the maximum working pressure. You may also wish to fit gauges to show feed pump pressure, fuel tank pressure, the intermediate pressure between cylinders in compound or triple expansion engines and the condenser vacuum. (This last, being negative pressure, is usually measured in inches of mercury, abbreviated to "Hg).

If the working pressure reaches the maximum working level, the *safety valve* will open, releasing excess steam. It must be able to take the full flow which the boiler can give and will also be checked by the boiler inspector.

Should all fail, there must be a last line of defence against serious boiler damage. This is the fusible plug - a brass or steel plug at the bottom of the boiler drum with a hole through the middle filled with lead. If you are unwise enough to go off to the pub leaving a good fire and the damper open, after a time the safety valve will lift. Eventually, if you don't return, the water level will drop so far that parts of the drum near the fire will become dry and will overheat. The lead melts and drops the remainder of water onto the fire. With any luck, this should prevent serious damage occurring.

Inspection

The SBA requires inspection certificates for most types of boiler. Inspectors like to know a lot about a boiler, its designer and its maker. If you are thinking of making a boiler (or having one made), involve the Inspector right from the design stage. You will find his/her advice invaluable.

5. **BOILER OPERATION**

There is a belief among the uninitiated that boilers are liable to "blow up" at the slightest provocation with disastrous results. The bystander will often display his fear by asking straight out if this is likely and will run a mile if there is a sudden escape of steam.

It need hardly be said that given the right set of conditions such a catastrophe *could* occur.

It is no less a fact that there have been boilers around for a very long time and the instances of explosions have, mercifully, been few.

What causes a boiler to explode? In the majority of cases mis-management and the failure of the operator to follow the recognised code of practice can be blamed.

The first requirement for safety is a properly designed and constructed boiler. The majority of steam boat enthusiasts do not construct, let alone design, their boilers. For the purpose of this article I am assuming that the boiler is in good order and to an established design.

Let us go through the procedure of preparing our boiler for a day out on the river.

We must first ensure that the correct level of water is in the boiler. You will notice that this is the first item to be considered. In fact the water level is the most important thing at all times. Loss of water level is the most serious emergency that can arise at any stage of the operation. There will be more to consider on this subject later.

The ideal level I suggest is half way up the glass. Some old timers will say a third, as the water expands on heating. This is true, but the extra water will be an asset when we first get steam for carrying out the tests which should be made.

Methods of firing vary, according to the fuel used, and the type of boiler, but do not be tempted to get steam too rapidly. Some boilers are more suited to rapid heating than others but in all cases a sudden rise in temperature causes local heating and different rates of expansion that does strain the boiler.

As soon as there is steam in the boiler the water gauge should be tested.

1. Close the top and bottom stop cocks and open the drain cock.

2. Open the top cock and steam should flow freely from the drain. You now know the top cock is not obstructed.
3. Close the drain cock. This pressurises the glass. Should it break no serious injury is likely, provided a protector is fitted. Steam is less likely to scald than water, which could escape if the bottom cock were opened first.
4. If the glass is satisfactory open the bottom cock; the water should rise rapidly to the correct level. Should it be sluggish in rising, the bottom passage through the fitting could be partially obstructed. If this is the case try opening the drain cock and closing again observing the rise in the level. Closing the top cock and repeating the draining may also help to dislodge an obstruction.

If all is well then, knowing the all important water gauge is functioning correctly proceed with steam raising.

If a malfunction is suspected then the fire must be drawn and the gauge examined before further steaming is attempted.

Before leaving the water gauge I feel that a few points should be considered. The novice might think that gauge glasses will last for ever, barring accidents. In fact tubular glasses do wear due to the action of minute particles of abrasive substance present in the feed water. The glass finally loses its strength and will burst.

The prudent engineer will change the glasses periodically. How often in the case of our boilers is problematical, but in the case of locomotives in steam for days at a time the LMSR used to change them at each boiler washout. The LNER were not so particular and breakages on the road were more frequent. Spares should always be carried and the operator should familiarise himself with the method of fitting. When opening up a newly fitted glass follow the test procedure already described.

A stout gauge glass protector should always be fitted. A careless knock with a fire iron could be disastrous. Should a glass break first close the bottom cock thus stopping the loss of scalding water.

Where test cocks are fitted as a standby method of checking water level these should next be tested. This serves two functions: it ensures that they are kept free in operation and also enables the operator to gain experience in their use. It is not easy to judge whether it is water or steam that escapes when a test cock is opened. By trying them when the normal is working the operator will be better able to rely on them should the need arise in earnest.

The next items on the check list are the means of feeding the boiler. First operate the hand pump. This standby is probably the most reliable means of feeding but should not be neglected.

Next comes the injector. Injectors are highly efficient but can be tricky to operate. Remember no injector will work if it is too hot. A leaking steam valve will heat the injector and unless it can be cooled it will not operate. Most are so fitted that cool feed water can be allowed to run through the overflow thus effecting the necessary cooling. Failing this water poured over the injector will often do the trick. An injector will only feed that amount of water which it can handle in the conditions prevailing. The surplus will pass out through the overflow. This should be eliminated by regulating the water valve. A properly installed injector should feed dry. Hot feed water will however cause loss at the overflow as will dirty cones in the injector itself.

Pumps of the Weir or Worthington types and those having cranks should next be considered. The former should be self starting and failure to do so is often due to the valve sticking. A *light* tap with a suitable tool will often free the valve but do not take the coal hammer to it as the fault might be more serious. It certainly would become so!

The crank types will require a turn to start them.

A good indication as to whether the pump is feeding can be obtained by checking the temperature of the clack or check valve through which the feed is entering the boiler. Be careful but if water is flowing you should be able to place your finger on the clack without discomfort.

Reasons for pump failure, apart from sticking valves, are few but a leaking clack or check valve will allow steam to form in the valve box of the pump and this will effectively cause an "airlock" or should it be "steamlock".

Engine driven feed pumps can only be tested when the engine is turning but do not neglect to carry out a functional check before leaving the mooring.

Having now proved that the means of ascertaining and maintaining the all important water level are all working correctly the pressure should be brought up until the safety valves either operate or can be eased. Some valves have an easing lever which enables the spring pressure to be overcome manually. The valve should lift and discharge easily. If the valve operates due to pressure, check that the pressure gauge is giving the proper reading. Any discrepancy should be investigated. If in doubt do not assume that it is the gauge that is at fault! Play safe, if the gauge reads low then assume the safety valve to be correct until proven otherwise. If the gauge reads high assume it to be correct and ease off the safety valve! Care should be exercised in this operation and if there is any doubt whatever draw the fire and drop the pressure first.

With these simple test procedures carried out to satisfaction you can get under weigh with the knowledge that barring any faults that may develop, your boiler is in good order.

If a fault does occur it is most likely to be an escape of steam due to a joint blowing out or maybe a check valve sticking open. Remember a loss of steam is a loss of water so the first action must always be to make good the loss by operating either the pumps or the injector. This action will also cool the boiler and reduce the pressure. Having thus taken action to protect the boiler and those aboard, investigate the fault. If there is any doubt at all draw the fire. Safety First!

Many of the boats that are with us today tend to be over boilered. That is, the boiler is capable of producing steam faster than the engine can use it. This is a pity as much of the skill and fun that can be had from operating a well balanced plant is lost. Yet others tend to be under boilered which can be very frustrating. But given sufficient thought these difficulties can be overcome to some extent.

A boiler is little more than a means of producing and storing heat energy in the form of steam. As the pressure rises so does the temperature and the energy available for use.

To judge from the vast amounts of steam and thus water and heat that are lost through safety valves at some events this is not always fully understood. Let us now consider some of the finer points.

There are various methods of controlling the amount of heat and is produced. Manipulation of dampers and the rate at which fuel is fired suffice on a condensing plant plus the judicious use of a stack blower or fan if one is fitted. On a puffer the exhaust steam is used to induce a flow of gases proportionate to the steam used and thus to the work done.

The oil burner, being so readily controlled, is fairly simple to operate but the coal burner requires a far greater degree of skill and in my opinion more interest.

Firing coal can be a messy business and is apt to produce a lot of smoke. This is indicative of inefficiency and loss of the heat in the fuel. If possible try firing to one side of the grate at a time. This allows the bright coals on one side to burn off the smoke produced by the "green" fire on the other. Firing to a clear stack is the hallmark of a good fireman! The regulation of air to the top of the fire, via the door damper, will also help but do not allow too much air to enter in this way as the cooling action will affect steaming and could cause tube leakage. Only in an emergency should the fire door be kept open.

When to fire? Little and often is the old watchword, but try to keep the fire only as thick as necessary to ensure that the grate is covered. Holes in a fire cause clinkering and apart from leading to poor steaming, tube leakage due to the flow of cold air is also possible.

When the steam pressure starts to approach the point where the safety valves will lift, and cause loss of water, is as good a time as any to stoke. The addition of coal will cool the firebox, thus avoiding the blowing off, and will permit fresh coals to become heated and start to burn ready to produce heat when needed. Provided that there is adequate fire on the grate it is never wise to add fuel when the pressure is falling. Once under way a marine plant operates under constant load and the skilled operator should be able to balance his firing to suit the demands of the engine.

When approaching a lock or other stopping place anticipate the coming reduction in steam requirements. Reduce the rate of firing and allow the pressure to drop. Top up the water level as high as possible so that should the safety valves lift during the stoppage there is not likely to be an embarrassing loss of water.

Once the engine is stopped then make up the fire by banking up one side. This reduces smoke emission. It also allows a quantity of coal to heat up so that when the time comes to move off the fire can be spread with the rake thus giving an immediate response to the renewed demand for steam.

The use of dampers is also governed by a few common sense rules. Stack dampers are used on coal burners but never on oil burners. While ashpan dampers common on oil burners are not used a great deal on coal burners. Apart from when the fires are banked up over a long period. The ashpan dampers can easily cause the firebars to be burned as these rely on the free flow of cool air to prevent burning. Basically dampers are used to regulate the flow of air for combustion. If the boiler is required to burn fuel at a faster rate, more air is necessary so open the damper and vice versa.

Your own boiler will have its own peculiarities but the basic principles will be the same as all the others.

At the end of the day it is a good idea to first fill the boiler to the top of the glass and then open the blow down valve.

Blow off half the glass of water. This will clear any sludge that may have accumulates in the bottom of the boiler.

Then fill again to the level that you would wish to have when steam is next raised.

You may wish to draw the fire or alternatively allow it to die naturally. The latter course allows slower cooling of the boiler which is good but ensure that the fire is indeed going out before you leave. To further the slow cooling a stack cover is a good thing to have. Even a piece of flat tile or metal will do. This prevents the natural draught from carrying cold air through the boiler. It will also stop rain from entering.

Some boilers fill themselves with water, drawn from the feed tank, at the moment when the steam condenses insude thus creating a vacuum. If the pressure has dropped sufficiently it is acceptable to open a valve e.g. the steam injector valve to prevent this. I have a simple ball valve fitted to do the job automatically.

Finally, remember that the water level is the most important thing any boiler operator has to watch. It is essential and above all else in importance. Loss of steam or fire is not a hazard. Embarrassing it may be, but never hazardous. Loss of water has been the major cause of boiler explosions since time began and will be in the future. Do not be caught out, it could be fatal.

To coin a corny rhyme:

> Water in doubt?
> Throw the fire out!

Good steaming.

6. **BRASS AND BRONZE POLISHING**

If you use your boat on the sea or you have failed to keep on top of your metal polishing you will know how difficult it is to remove the tarnish before getting down to the bright metal. A quick solution is to use one of the paint rubbing down pads that are on the market now. They are made of stiff plastic sponge coated with a carborundum powder in three grades. The finest grade should be used for brass and bronze, followed by a final polish with Brasso, Bluebell or Duraglit. Whilst on the subject, these pads are excellent for preparing varnish - the medium grade being used wet.

7. OIL BURNERS

Introduction

Although lighting a fire in a boiler to heat the water that it contains appears to be a very simple concept it is helpful to start with a clear understanding of just what is happening when we apply the match.

Heat Transfer

Three forms of heat transfer have to be considered:-

1. Radiation in which heat travels in straight lines through a vacuum or gas.

2. Conduction in which heat travels by contact.

3. Convection in which heat is conveyed by moving liquids or gasses as a result of reducing density as their temperature increases.

Source of Heat

This falls into two groups:-

1. Solids, e.g. coal, coke, wood.

2. Vapours, e.g. oil, gas.

The only major difference between the two is that solids burn in two stages. On heating they release vapours which burn above the bed in the same way as the second group, but at the same time the bed becomes incandescent giving off radiant heat as it changes into ash.

Boiler Design

This means that a boiler designed for burning solids will have a firebox designed to take advantage of the radiant and conducted heat from the embers. The vapours released will be burnt in a combustion chamber mainly designed to take advantage of the conducted heat from the flames and hot gases. It is therefore obvious that in the case of boilers designed for vapour burning, a firebox in the true sense of the word will be of little value.

Heating Surface

In comparing the evaporative powers of a boiler it is not sufficient to estimate simply the total heating surface, consisting as it does of furnace, combustion chamber, tubes etc., because the powers of transmission of these surfaces differ greatly.

In an experiment placing a heat source in the centre of a steel box submerged in water, it was found that the upper surface generated heat more than twice as fast as the vertical sides, per unit of area, whilst the lower face yielded none. The poor efficiency of the sides was due to the difficulty with which steam bubbles separate from the vertical surfaces to give place to fresh particles of water, thus allowing the build-up of a thin film of non-conducting steam.

Best Design for Burning Vapour

This leads us to the conclusion that the way to get the best heat transfer out of burning vapour is to employ water tubes as near to the horizontal as practical. Compromise is however essential in order to ensure circulation by convection; around 5% to 10% incline is the optimum. We can also see why grate area in coal firing is such a critical factor in that the amount of related horizontal heating surface will give greater efficiency.

Fire tubes can also be very disappointing in their performance as can be seen from a naval experiment of 1846 with a horizontal multi-tubular boiler five feet long. In the first inch of tube length 46 units were evaporated, 47 units in the next 10 inches, followed by 30, 22, 18, 17 units in the remaining four 12 inch sections. It would be slightly more evenly distributed in a vertical fire-tube boiler but the effective heat transfer will be reduced in the tubes for the reason already stated. Forced draught also improves distribution.

The Flame

The other critical factors in vapour burning are complete combustion and length of flame and it is interesting to consider how we can control these factors. The appearance of the flame is the best guide and the indications can be recognised as follows in the case of paraffin or kerosene:-

1. **Fuel temperature**

(a) Too hot - it will flash instead of burning.
(b) Correct - it will burn steadily when mixed with air.
(c) Too cool - it will dribble out of the jet with a dull, yellow, spluttery, smokey flame.

2. **Fuel pressure**

(a) Too high - will give a noisy, fierce, blue lean flame, often too short to reach the tubes.
(b) Correct - will give a long white flame rimmed with blue at its base (the blue is not always so apparent with the heavier kerosene). Noise will be a low roar.

(c) Too low - will give a silent smokey yellow flame.

3. **Air mixture**

(a) Lean mixtures - burn with a very noisy fierce blue unstable flame.
(b) Correct mixtures - burn with a long white flame with a narrow blue base and a low roar.
(c) Rich mixtures - burn with a smokey yellow silent flame.

Fuel Temperature

This will be dependant on the size and design of the fuel heating element and although complicated cast types have been used, by far the most common takes the form of a coil mounted above a flame spreader.

The most common material for the coil is solid drawn mild steel fully annealed for ease of working. Its wall thickness should be ⅛" with ¼" bore for small units, ⅜" bore for larger ones. Small would be for boilers with an evaporation rate below 200 lb/hr at 150 psi. The length of tube in the coil should be 10 feet for these conditions. It may be adjusted by 3" per 10 lb/hr evaporation rate in either direction.

The coil will be cone shaped approx. 6" dia at the top and at an angle of not less than 45° to the path of the flame. The centre line of the bottom turn should match the diameter of the top edge of the domed spreader. In a centre drum boiler the size of the top coil can be adjusted to match the drum diameter, but its length must be maintained.

Fuel Pressure

This will be influenced by jet size which should be between 0.050" and 0.080". For 200 lb/hr evaporation rate at 150 psi good results will be achieved with a 0.075" jet and a fuel pressure of 25 psi. This of course assumes that the boiler efficiency is good.

In setting up the burner remember that when adjusting pressure an increase will increase noise and reduce smoke, and a decrease will reduce noise and promote smoke. Thus the best setting will be just above the onset of smoke with a margin for falling pressure if you have a hand pumped system. A further indication of correct setting will be a white flame with a tinge of blue at its base.

Mixture

In the simple Lune Valley type of burner, air take-up is controlled by the distance between the jet and the spreader. The greater distance the fuel travels as a gas the more air it can absorb. The best results will be obtained when the distance is about 1". Small adjustments may be necessary when testing. An increase in the gap increases noise, reduces smoke and promotes the desirable blue fringe. An excessive gap would turn more than half the flame blue, accompanied by instability to the point of going out. A great improvement can be made to the design by fitting an adjustable air inlet round the jet combined with a short venturi tube on the lines of a bunsen burner. The diagram shows the general arrangement of such a burner. The venturi should be ¼" bore at its base (surrounding the jet). Over the ⅜" length where the air holes enter it should taper down to 3/16" and run parallel for ½" ending in a square nose. In the set-up, this should be 1" from the spreader as described above.

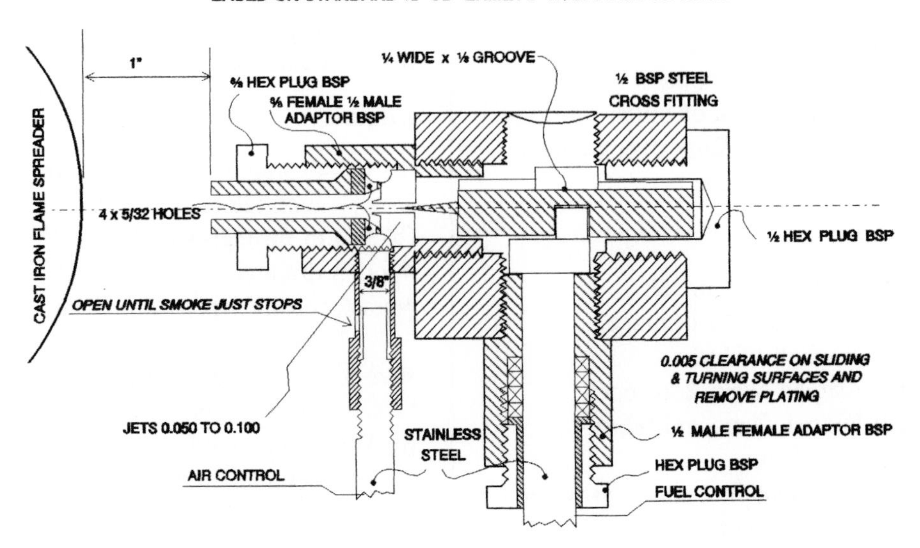

8. CHECK LIST

Preparation

Hull:

(a) Visual damage check.
(b) Warps, anchor, lock windlass, first aid kit, fire extinguishers, bailer, life jackets, oars etc. available and in good condition.

Propeller:

(a) Secure and free from weed.
(b) Clear of bottom.

Steering:

(a) Visual check on cables etc.
(b) Full and free travel.

Engine:

(a) Throttle shut.
(b) Mid-gear.
(c) Drain cocks open.
(d) Visual check of bolts, bearings etc., turning over by hand if possible.

Boiler:

(a) Firebars and bricks clear and in place.
(b) No sign of leaks.
(c) Ashpan clear, door open.
(d) Funnel, flues and tubes clear.
(e) Sufficient fuel and feed water for journey.
(f) Stopvalve and blowdown shut.
(g) Safety valve free.
(h) Feed cocks open.
(i) All gauge cocks to normal (usually vertical).
(j) Test hand-pump, water in glass.

LIGHT UP!

Departure

Boiler:

(a) Blow down water gauge:
- steam arm shut (horizontal), open drain briefly,
- return steam arm to normal,
- repeat for water arm,
- check all cocks returned to vertical,
- water level should bounce back to original level.

(b) Water level, fire and pressure high.
(c) Stop valve fully open.

Engine:

(a) Oil all round, fill and turn on lubricators.
(b) Warm through slowly:
- open drain cocks,
- crack throttle open approx ¼ turn,
- rock valve gear until engine turns freely.

(c) With compounds, warm LP cylinder first with simpling

valve open, then repeat with it closed.

CAST OFF!

Leaving Boat

Boiler:

Anticipate stop if possible:
(a) Raise water level to top of glass.
(b) Bank up fire for short stay or burn out.
(c) Shut draught and open firebox door slightly to prevent blowing off.
(d) Shut stop valve and feed valves.

Engine:

(a) Mid gear.
(b) Drain cocks open.
(c) Lubricators off.

Mooring:

(a) Ensure clear water under hull.
(b) Warps secure and free enough to allow for tide and wash.

BOILER DIFFICULTIES

Water level

Glass empty:

(a) Dump fire into wet ashpan or overboard.
(b) Ease safety valve until pressure drops.
(c) Blow down water gauge to check.

Glass low:

(a) Close ashpan damper or turn burner off.
(b) Increase feed using hand-pump etc. if engine feed pump appears defective.
(c) Blow down water gauge to check.
(d) Check feed lines, including hull inlets, strainers, etc.

Glass too high:

(a) Stop feed.
(b) If priming: slow engine and open drain cocks, use auxiliary steam and/or blow down to reduce boiler level.

With a condensing plant:

If hotwell is overflowing, suspect condenser leak: condensate will taste salty if at sea.

Poor Fire

(a) Too deep: Blower on, don't rake, burn wood until coal reduced.
(b) Clinkered up or full ashpan: rake out, clear up.
(c) other possibilities: sooted up, blower blocked, draught leaking.

9. **COAL**

It is surprising how many people think of coal as simply a black substance that is dug out of the ground, and do not realise how many different varieties there are, and what they are, or are not suitable for. In this article I explain briefly why coals differ and what effects the differences have; I mention the importance of the Clean Air legislation and I say something about the availability and pricing of different coals and manufactured solid fuels. Finally, for those who are in a position to experiment, I draw attention to some recent application of Porta's Gas Producer combustion system, which is, among other things, a way of reducing fuel costs.

Coals were produced by the action of pressure and heat over æons of time on rotting vegetation that had accumulated in swamps that were buried under the earth millions of years ago. The different intensities of pressure and heat, along with the different lapses of time since the burial of various deposits can account for the different basic types of coal.

Excluding ash and moisture, the main chemical constituents of all coals are carbon, hydrogen and oxygen; their proportions vary and it is found that a very useful ranking of coals can be made on the basis of the percentages of carbon and hydrogen the coal substances themselves contain.

The youngest coals are *lignites*. Not normally available in Britain, these are ranked the lowest; they have the lowest calorific value and contain the least carbon. They have a high content of volatile matter, are very reactive, may ignite spontaneously and should certainly be avoided. *Bituminous* coals come next in rank; they include various coals sold under the name of *house coal*. Compared with the lignites they all contain more carbon but their content of volatile matter is not as high. When suitably free from ash they have high to very high calorific values. Although they will not ignite spontaneously when kept in small heaps they can be ignited fairly easily. On a traditional grate they burn with a flame that remains long and bright but rather smoky until most of the volatile matter has been driven off. Some of these coals tend to form a cake on the grate. Because of their tendency to make smoke it is illegal to burn bituminous coals (i.e. house coals) on a traditional grate in an officially designated Smoke Control area.

(No solid fuel or oil of any kind may be burnt in a 'Smokeless Zone' which is not the same as a Smoke Control Area. There are only two Smokeless Zones in Britain - in London and Manchester.)

This law certainly applies to steam launches and it means that if your steam launch does not have a specially adapted and officially approved grate and firebox for burning bituminous coal smokelessly it should either be fuelled only by one of the authorised smokeless fuels, or not enter a Smoke Control Area. The law would, for example, affect the use of bituminous coals such as Yorkshire *hards* or East Midlands *hards*, even though these would otherwise be suitable, as they were formerly used for railway locomotives - mainly because of their relative freedom from clinkering.

Higher in rank than bituminous coals come the *sub-bituminous* coals including a group of naturally "smokeless" fuels - the *Welsh 'Dry' Steam Coals*. (The 'dry' refers to the fact that they do not exude any liquid product of decomposition when heated; it has nothing to do with the quality of the steam.) Welsh dry steam coals have yet more carbon but less hydrogen and other volatile matter than bituminous coals, hence their flame is short and relatively smokeless, albeit bright. Their calorific value is high and they are non-caking or only slightly caking.

Proceeding in the direction of yet higher rank (more carbon, less hydrogen) we come to two more groups of authorised smokeless fuels; firstly the *Semi-Anthracites* and finally the highest rank of all, the *Anthracites*. Both groups have high calorific values. Anthracites, having the lowest content of volatile matter, can be fairly difficult to light; they are rather dense and slow-burning and may not be easy to get burning vigorously again after a fire has been 'slumbering'.

It is probable that the Welsh dry steam coal is still the best solid fuel for steam launches, followed by semi-anthracite and then anthracite. The manufactured, as opposed to the naturally smokeless, fuels however deserve to be listed as you would be within the law by using them. They include *Phurnacite*, *Homefire*, *Sunbrite*, *Coalite* and *Rexco*. (Coke from gasworks is no longer available). Sunbrite can be ruled out as it cannot be 'slumbered', being too unreactive. Homefire comes in briquettes weighing about 225g (about half a pound) apiece. Phurnacite, Coalite and Rexco can be obtained in a variety of sizes. (I should mention that the same is true of the naturally smokeless fuels.) *Housewarm* is a specially prepared bituminous house coal - i.e. it is not an authorised smokeless fuel and it should not be confused with Homefire.

The prices of all the fuels mentioned above vary surprisingly widely across the country, so that if you require a substantial quantity such as a lorry load, it may pay you to drive a considerable distance for it. Any coal merchant should be prepared to quote by telephone. However, not all varieties are available everywhere.

As smokeless fuels tend to cost a good deal more than house coal - at least half as much again in many places and, as you are allowed to burn bituminous coal in a Smoke Control Area if you do so in an approved or 'exempted' appliance, there is a strong incentive to seek savings in fuel costs by devising an 'exempted' appliance for a steam launch. To show how this might be done I will consider firstly the domestic type of smoke-reducing appliance based on the downdraught principle, and then the conventional railway locomotive fire-box. I will describe and recommend Porta's gas producer combustion system for trial in a steamboat; it has already been proved successful on rail.

The downdraught principle whereby smoke-reducing combustion of bituminous coals can be achieved was invented hundreds of years ago, but its widespread exploitation in houses is a phenomenon of the last decade.

The fire is refuelled from above in the usual way, but the smoke from the fresh fuel is drawn down through the fire and so is mostly burnt up before reaching the boiler or flue connection to the chimney. As far as I know, the principle has not yet been applied to any steam launch and it would obviously be a major task to do so.

Coal-fired steam railway locomotives had a bad reputation for making smoke, but a good deal of this was avoidable. There is a great deal of fascinating lore of the way steam locomotives responded to coal from the different collieries, but here there is only space to say that, given skilled firing, a surprising freedom from smoke could be obtained, even when certain bituminous coals were in use, though others were definitely unsuitable. With a selected bituminous coal such as Yorkshire 'hards', the intense heat and turbulence of the gases in the large fire box, assisted by radiation from the brick arch, burnt up much of the smoke. Cooling the fire-box by putting too much coal on at a time of course led to the production of too much smoke. Some launches have locomotive type boilers and fireboxes, albeit very small ones. I feel that the small size must render the equipment more liable to make smoke; it would be interesting to hear of owners' experiences on this.

It would be interesting to try Porta's Gas producer combustion system in a steam launch. It is a simple development from a normal locomotive type fire-box. It could be applied to a vertical boiler too. The main differences from normal are that extra air is provided between the fire box and the brick arch, reducing the draught across the fire bed; exhaust steam is led into the ashpan to be drawn into the fire bed. The extra air comes in through carefully placed holes around the firebox just above the fire bed. The main consequence is that the fire bed acts more as a gasifier than as a combustor; the gases and smoke arising from the bed are then burnt up very efficiently in the high turbulence created by the extra air coming in all round the box. The principle can be seen at work in the locomotive **River Esk** operated by the Ravenglass and Eskdale Railway in Cumbria. This locomotive operates virtually smokelessly on a mixture of semi-anthracite fuels and a naturally smoky bituminous coal of larger size; it has saved the company a considerable sum in fuel costs since its conversion in 1983.

In 1985 the principle was applied to the locomotive **Linda** on the Ffestiniog Railway. That experiment is showing that high ash coals and caking coals are not suitable, but that virtually smokeless combustion of a non-caking, low ash bituminous coal has indeed been achieved.

Anyone conducting experiments on burning bituminous coals is advised to seek the advice of the local authority's environmental control staff who are empowered to exempt an appliance from the requirement to burn an authorised smokeless fuel on evidence that it can burn other fuels with smoke reduction, or in furtherance of experiments in search of such evidence.

The opinions expressed here are those of the author and not necessarily those of British Coal.

10. THE CONDENSER

Purpose:

To condense the exhaust steam from the engine back to water, so that it can be re-used in the boiler. Also, to reduce the pressure at the engine exhaust, to improve the power and efficiency of the plant.

Principle:

Steam leaving the cylinder is passed through a pipe, or system of pipes, which are cooled on the other side. The steam condenses to water, and runs to the lowest point of the condenser, from where a pump (the extraction or air pump) removes it, usually to the hot well. The feed pump then puts it back into the boiler.

In steam boats, the condenser is usually cooled by an external water flow, although in some applications an air flow may be used (in a similar set-up to a car radiator), and in others a jet of cold water is injected into the steam. The simplest arrangement is the keel-cooler; a pipe runs under the hull, often close to the keel or bilge keel for protection, and is cooled by the passing flow. A typical small launch installation might have about 20 feet of tubing, around 1 inch diameter. The alternative arrangement is the inboard condenser where the cooling (or circulating) water is pumped through a bank of pipes which pass through an iron or steel vessel containing the exhaust steam. This requires an auxiliary circulating pump, but is less vulnerable than the keel-cooler.

The pump which removes the water is the extraction pump. However, the water volume is very small, and there is usually a considerable quantity of air (arising from leaks, or from solution in the water) to remove as well. Some installations use a separate air pump, but usually one pump is designed to be capable of both duties simultaneously. It is then described as the air pump.

Operation:

For the water re-use role, there is really nothing more to say. The advantages of re-using water are that you do not need to keep finding new supplies, and you get less scale in the boiler. The disadvantages are that you cannot puff, and you may have to remove cylinder oil from the feed water.

The extra efficiency arises primarily because you can get more pressure difference across the engine. Instead of exhausting to atmospheric pressure, you can let the large reduction in volume of the steam as it condenses reduce the pressure to (say) 10 lb/sq inch below atmospheric, and then pump the water out of the condenser. With a supply pressure of 100 lb/sq inch, this could produce a significant increase in power for a given engine and boiler. It can be shown from thermodynamic theory that you get that extra power for a relatively small increase in fuel consumption (to drive the air pump). Compound engines, in particular, benefit from condenser vacuum, since you are trying to split a rather small pressure drop between two cylinders.

To maintain a good vacuum in the condenser (incidentally, usually measured in inches of Mercury below atmospheric - 2 inches of Mercury is about the same as 1 lb/sq inch) you need an extremely well sealed condenser and pump. Since the volume of the water you are pumping out is only about 1/2000 th of the volume of steam going in, pinhole leaks can be catastrophic. Many people use diaphragm pumps (which need no seal round the pump rod) for this reason. A reasonable level of vacuum to aim at is 17-20 inches.

11. COMPOUNDING

Purpose:

To separate the expansion of the steam into two stages, enabling higher pressures to be used without impossibly long strokes or small clearances. There may also be a slight improvement in the efficiency of the plant.

Principle:

When steam expands in the cylinder, driving the piston down and doing useful work, its volume increases considerably. An ideal expansion from 100 psi to atmospheric would involve an increase in volume of about 6.25 times (real expansions are not ideal, and the ratio will be a little larger, but the principle is the same). This then must be the ratio of the cylinder volume at admission cut-off to that at steam release to exhaust (the expansion ratio), if all the available work is to be extracted.

These volumes consist of the swept volume of the cylinder (or a portion of it) and the 'dead' space above the piston at top dead centre and in the valve passages. To get a high expansion ratio, the dead space must be minimised and the swept volume maximised. The valve passages cannot be made too small without adding extra losses. Increasing the cylinder diameter will increase the dead space above it, so the only real choice is to increase the stroke, which leads to numerous other problems. The ratio of 6.25 is not too difficult to achieve, but if we increase the pressure to 150 psi and exhaust to a condenser at 20 inches vacuum, the ideal ratio becomes about 24, which is getting rather hard.

The solution to the problem is to avoid the large pressure ratio in one cylinder by splitting the expansion between two or more cylinders. If, for example, the High Pressure cylinder drops the pressure from 150 psi to 15 psi, and then hands the steam over to the Low Pressure cylinder which drops it to 20 inches vacuum, the HP requires an expansion ratio of about 4.5, and the LP of about 5.4, both quite feasible. Since the volume of steam entering the LP is 4.5 times that entering the HP, it needs to be larger. In this case, about 1.7 times the diameter would be appropriate. An engine working on this principle is called a Compound engine.

The same principle can be extended to triple and quadruple

expansion engines, which spread the expansion over 3 or 4 cylinders, respectively.

The above discussion is much idealized. The actual choice of cylinder dimensions and pressures must take into account departures from ideal conditions, pressure losses in valves and the pipe connecting the two cylinders (the 'receiver'), the proportion of power developed in the two cylinders (an equal split is desirable), and many other things. But most practical designs come out with a cylinder diameter ratio around 1.5 to 2.

It is a firm belief of owners that a compound engine is more efficient than a simple engine working over the same pressure range. There are no grounds for this, provided that both engines are working at their design conditions. The statement is really a tautology; a Compound is more efficient under the conditions for which it was designed, when there are problems in making a Simple work efficiently. The opposite is also true.

Operation:

Compounding is introduced to make use of a higher pressure drop. A compound engine will not work properly except near its design boiler and condenser pressures. If the boiler pressure drops, the expansion ratio of the HP stays the same, so the HP outlet pressure drops. It may in fact drop below condenser pressure, and the LP then becomes an extraction pump, getting the steam out of the HP and increasing its pressure to condenser pressure. The LP produces negative power - you would be better off without it. So it is essential to have three gauges - boiler pressure, intermediate (receiver) pressure and vacuum. It may be possible to allow for off-design pressures to some extent by adjusting the cut off.

A compound engine is not necessarily self-starting. The steam is only applied to the HP, which can get stuck on dead centre. So a 'simpling valve' is usually fitted. This allows boiler steam into the receiver and so to the LP. If the HP is on dead centre, the LP won't be, and the engine will start.

12. **COPPER PIPE PRECAUTIONS**

Copper pipes work harden in use and, if they are subject to vibration, they will be liable to fracture after two or three years. It is a good idea to anneal them every third year. Simply heat with a gas blow lamp until they become cherry red - then plunge into water. They should bend easily after this treatment and won't fracture.

13. **BENDING AND JOINING COPPER PIPES**

When training at WH Allen's building steam engines and turbines, the students favoured the pattern shop and the coppersmith's workshop above all others. Perhaps it was because they were dependent on old skills and craftsmanship.

George the foreman was indeed a master craftsman who could work miracles in bronze and copper and he always boasted that it was the copper pipework that gave that final touch of quality to the appearance of an engine. Pipe fittings were clumsy and expensive and to be avoided if at all possible in favour of graceful right angle bends, straight and parallel runs and silver soldered flared branch connections. Compression fittings were totally unacceptable being suitable for use by plumbers not coppersmiths.

I am very relieved that George cannot see **SAUMAREZ**'s engine which is now festooned with temporary pipework, the result of endless experiments. Nevertheless, it may be helpful to give an idea of how George went about his task in order to help those who are more certain of their designs and concerned about appearances.

First decide on the range of copper tube that you are going to use, which may well be fixed by what is readily available. I suggest:-

¼", ⅜", ½"	20 gauge
¾", 1"	16 gauge

These should bend without kinking if fully annealed by heating to cherry red and quenching in water. Do not attempt to bend to radii of less than tube outside diameter × 5 and do use a former such as a V-belt pulley that gives side support. In the case of the larger pipes a coppersmith, in order to achieve perfection, would fill the tube with dry sand and plug each end with tapered hardwood bungs making sure that no air space was left unfilled. Larger pipes may require annealing between stages of manipulation because copper work-hardens rapidly.

Where unions were essential silver soldered nipples were the order of the day. The best approach is to flux and silver the inside of the nipple. Clean and flux the pipe then heat the assembly and push together. This should give a clean joint with a neat fillet of solder at the edge of the fitting. When heating, make sure that the pipe gets up to solder melting point which will be indicated by the absence of a meniscus where it joins the pipe.

The ultimate in coppersmith's art is the palm joint which allows junctions to be made at any angle and between different pipe sizes with a very tidy appearance. The procedure is to flare the annealed end of the joining pipe to produce a trumpet-like flange twice pipe diameter for small flanges, reducing to one and a half times for the larger sizes. A piece of metal round bar the same size as the main pipe is required as a former. Anneal the flange again, lay the former across it at the angle required and with a small soft hammer tap the flange into conformity with it. To facilitate this operation grip the former in a vice and hold the pipe by hand. The outside edge of the palm or flange should be cleaned up with a file. In some cases its appearance may be improved by making it oval.

To complete the job drill the main pipe to branch ID and flux the surrounding pipe surface to an area slightly larger than the palm. Flux and generously silver solder the joint surface of the palm, then hold in place and heat the entire assembly until the solder witness appears on the main pipe surface all round the edge of the palm. If you wish to silver solder a large complex group of branches at the same time, for example setting them to several connections to an engine, drill and tap for a small countersunk screw in each palm, thus holding it in position for test assembly. Then proceed as above and screw together again after soldering the joint surfaces of the palms. Recheck the fitting on the engine then complete the operation by heating, either on the engine or removed if heating *in situ* presents difficulties.

14. DRILLING THIN METAL

Using an ordinary twist drill often results in an almost triangular hole. Drilling through another piece of metal will help but there is still a risk of hole distortion. A sure answer is to use a centre drill. These are readily available from good tool shops and in appearance they are stepped drills ground to the standard 60° to match the centre on a lathe.

15. THE EJECTOR

Purpose:

The Ejector is one of a family of devices known as jet pumps. They use the energy of one fluid (in our case usually steam) to move another (air or water). (The other main type is the Injector which will be the subject of another note on its own.) The ejector has no moving parts, and so is fairly reliable. It is mainly used for sucking rather than pressurizing.

Principle:

A jet of fluid, i.e. liquid, vapour or gas, from a nozzle is highly turbulent and tends to drag along (entrain) fluid from its surroundings. The jet may either discharge into a large volume (open jet, figure 1) or into a specially shaped contracting-expanding nozzle (enclosed jet, figure 2). A familiar example of the open jet type is the Bunsen burner or its domestic version, the gas stove, which mixes gas with air. The laboratory water-tap driven vacuum pump is an enclosed jet type. Ejectors are not at all efficient in their use of energy and so are not normally used as part of the main power plant, though they have sometimes been used for condenser extraction pumps (e.g. at the Bobbin Mill, Stott Park, Cumbria).

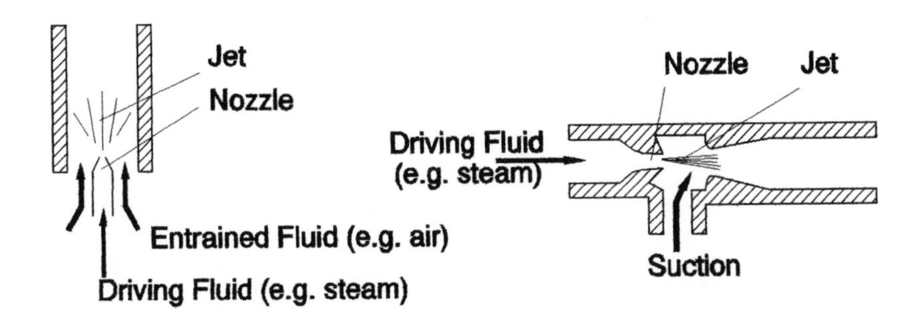

Figure 1
Open Jet Ejector

Figure 2
Enclosed Jet Ejector

Operation:

The most common applications on small steamboats are for bilge pumps (enclosed jet) and for fire draught (open jet). The main things to remember with a Bilge Ejector are to fit a strainer to keep coal dust, ash, etc. out of the water inlet, to provide a hole in the floor to clear the strainer when the polishing rag gets in it, and to discharge the bilge water over the side above the water line.

For fire draught, you can either use exhaust steam through a *Blast Pipe* or live steam through a *Blower* nozzle. A blast pipe is simply an exhaust pipe pointing up the funnel. The outlet is as large as possible, consistent with good entrainment, to avoid putting back pressure on the engine. A blower nozzle, on the other hand, is a small steam pipe pointing up the funnel. Its outlet is the smallest that will give adequate draught, to avoid using too much steam. As an example, **SENTA**'s blast pipe is 13 mm in diameter, whereas the blower is under 1 mm. Both these were designed by the well-proven method of trying what happens to be around, and then not messing about with things that work.

16. **ENGINES**

Finding your engine: it is safer to err on the side of a little too much power. There will always be losses you have not considered, and you can always throttle back a bit if you find you cannot use all the power available.

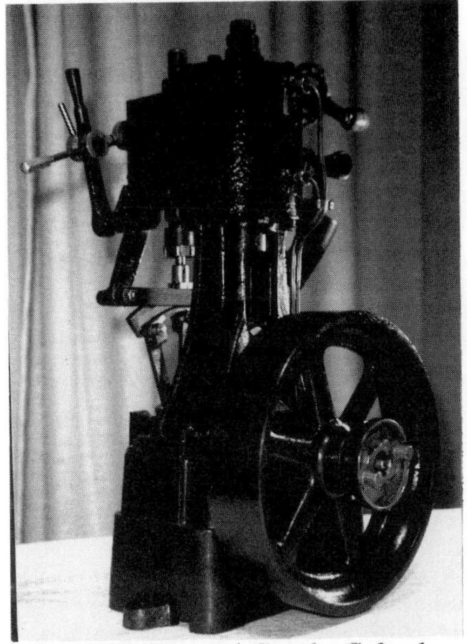

Stuart Turner 5A Single Cylinder Engine

Nearly all steam boats use engines of the *inverted* (i.e. cylinders above the crank), open frame (i.e. you can see the moving parts), reciprocating (i.e. up and down) type. But there is no reason not to have other types; a well known example of the enclosed type can be found in **SAUMAREZ V**, and of an inclined type in the small paddler **HERACLES**.

The only real alternative to the reciprocating engine is the steam turbine. Modern steamboats (mostly nuclear submarines) are invariably turbine driven, but small turbines are not easy to design, build or harness to a low-speed propeller. I know of no turbine-driven boat smaller than the original **TURBINIA** of 1895 (100 ft long, see the Newcastle Science Museum).

The reciprocating engine basically has two parts. In the first, the steam pressure acts on the piston inside the cylinder, forcing it alternately down and up (or to and fro in a horizontal engine) which in turn acts through the connecting rod onto the crank which converts the straight motion into rotation. The second part is the valve gear which lets the steam into the cylinder at the start of the stroke and out again near the end. All the other oddments stuck around the engine are, to a greater or lesser extent, optional extras. They may help make the engine to work better (e.g. lubricating systems), to start (drains or simpling valves) or have nothing to do with the engine itself (e.g. pumps).

The cylinder/valve gear unit is repeated several times in multi-cylinder engines. Some have near-identical units, while others, known as *compounds* (two cylinders of different sizes) and *triple expansion* (three cylinders of different sizes) do not. The steam let out of the smallest (the high pressure or HP) is passed to the next (the intermediate or IP in a triple) and then on to the biggest (the low pressure or LP). This has advantages for efficiency on large, well operated engines. On small engines, it looks quite pretty and may sometimes save a little steam. The usual practice on all these types is for steam to be fed onto the back of the piston at the end of its stroke to drive it back up again; such an engine is said to be *double acting*. I will not at this stage discuss *oscillating* engines, of which there are a few about. In these there is no connecting rod, the piston working directly on the crank. The cylinder itself pivots to allow this.

Stuart Turner Swan Twin High Pressure Engine

The purpose of the valve gear is to let the steam into and out of the cylinder at the right moments. This is fairly simple to arrange. However, it is usually called upon to be adjustable, so that the engine can be made to run backwards (which is cheaper than fitting a reverse gearbox), and sometimes to vary the amount of steam being admitted (the *cut-off*); this can improve efficiency under part load. These can make the problem of design more or less impossible - which explains why there are so many sorts around.

This is not the place to go into details, but the most common on boats is Stephenson's Link, which has a pair of eccentrics (wheels with the hole off-centre) for each cylinder, mounted on the crankshaft. These eccentrics, which move the valve up and down, are more or less opposite to each other on the shaft, so that by means of a curved *link,* one or other of them may be brought into play giving the ability to reverse. One also occasionally sees a *slip eccentric* where instead of two there is only one eccentric which, by means of a spiral groove, can be turned round on the shaft the necessary amount. Other valve gears one occasionally comes across are Hackworth's, Joy's and Marshall's, all of which are described in detail in FUNNELs 32, 33 and 34.

Rather than designing an engine (which few of us could do with any confidence) we will take the same approach as with the hull, and ask "will that one do?". For a new engine, the maker should be able to say what it can do. Otherwise, it is not too difficult to *estimate* the power from the cylinder bore and stroke (of the HP cylinder if it is a compound), engine speed (not necessarily the same as propeller speed) and steam pressure. We also need to know the number of cylinders and whether or not it is double acting (most are). The formula is:

Horizontal Engine

$$HP/c = \frac{A(p) \times S \times rpm \times P}{66{,}000}$$

where:

HP/c is the horsepower per cylinder,
A is the piston area in square inches,
S is the stroke in feet,
P is the steam pressure in lb/in^2.

To get the engine HP we multiply this by the number of HP cylinders, then by 2 if it is double acting, and finally by the Mechanical Efficiency. This last is a number which allows for the effects of friction and other losses in the engine itself, and is around 0.8 to 0.9.

As an example, let us estimate the power of the Stuart 'Cygnet' engine. It has one double acting cylinder of 2.25" bore and 2" stroke, working at 800 rpm with a steam pressure of 100 psi. The piston area comes out to 3.98 sq in and the horsepower per cylinder comes out at 0.8. Multiply by 2 for double-acting and by 0.85 for mechanical efficiency, and we get 1.36 HP - reasonably close to the 1.5 HP given in the Stuart Turner catalogue. The difference could come either from the value of Mechanical Efficiency used or from an underlying assumption in the formula for effective steam pressure.

Transmission

We now have a boat with a propeller on a shaft, and an engine. How do we connect the two? There are two things to consider. First, on most boats, the propeller shaft is inclined upwards and we either have to mount the engine on a slant to match up with it or put a bend in the transmission. Both approaches are widely used. Second, our engine and propeller do not necessarily want to run at the same speed (or, for that matter, in the same direction). If we have a large, slow engine and a small fast prop we want a speed increase (e.g. **MUDLARK**); a small engine will want a speed reduction to drive a big propeller (e.g. **SENTA**). Whatever the set-up, there *must* be a flexible connection somewhere. It is very difficult to align two shafts exactly and small boats are by no means rigid. Misalignment will put enormous loads on the bearings, leading to power loss, wear and noise. So somewhere there must be a coupling which allows a small amount of misalignment in both direction and position, including movement in the direction of the shaft. An added bonus of such a coupling is that it usually provides a quick-release point for disconnecting the drive when the engine is taken out.

Simpson Strickland Compound Engine

To match a horizontal shaft engine to an inclined shaft we can use a universal joint similar to those used in motor car transmissions. Better still, use a pair of them, which will allow misalignment in any direction. If one of them is on a spline (a set of grooves on its shaft so that it can slide lengthways) all our problems are solved. Alternatively, a bevel gear can be used as on the **JAMES WATT**, but these are not easy to design or make.

To connect an engine and shaft that are more or less in line, whether horizontal or inclined, many sorts of proprietary couplings are available. They mostly consist of two metal flanges with some kind of projections, with a rubber insert sandwiched between them. This may be held in position just by the flanges, or may actually be bolted through onto one or both of them.

To change the speed we can use gears, chains or belts. gears are very efficient (98% or better), but need accurate alignment and lubrication. A sealed oil bath gearbox (as on **SENTA**) is really the only practical solution. Chains, similar to bicycle chains, are about as efficient so long as they are kept clean and well oiled. If allowed to become dirty, they rapidly deteriorate and become inefficient and noisy. They are fairly fussy about alignment and tension, and have a tendency to snatch under unsteady loads. Belts come in two types - Vee belts like motor car fan belts, and toothed belts as on overhead camshaft drives and many small machines such as lawnmowers. They are very different animals. Vee belts are cheap and reasonably forgiving, but have a tendency to slip and are not very efficient. Toothed belts are a little more demanding as regards alignment, but they do not slip and are much more efficient. They are probably the answer to our problem.

Our engine is now correctly matched to the propeller. All that remains is to provide some steam to it - but that is another story.

17. **EMULSION ON HOT METAL**

Heat-resistant paint - I question whether there is anything which will stand up to a red hot funnel, but by chance I came across a simple solution that is worth trying.

I always use ordinary decorating vinyl emulsion to paint lagging and, lightly painted on the surface of asbestos mineral wool or glass fibre, it is ideal. After the first coat, several coats can be built up, giving a reasonably smooth and durable surface. I imagine that some of the new filled emulsions would be even better.

Last time I emulsioned my lagging on **SAUMAREZ**, I splashed the stainless steel boiler near the base of the funnel where it gets very hot. To my surprise, it stayed there brilliant white for many months and put up a very good fight when I eventually made a determined effort to remove it with a scraper. A test ring is going on the funnel this year.

18. **FLAG ETIQUETTE**

As I plan to launch my first steamboat in the spring, I have been looking into the question of flags. My investigations have revealed the following; members comments would be appreciated.

1. **The RED ENSIGN**

The most important flag worn by a boat, this flag indicates the boat's nationality, i.e. the boat's owner is a British subject. The ensign is also used for saluting.

Its length should be twice the hoist.

At sea the ensign may be worn day and night, but when in harbour the ensign should be hoisted at 0800 hours in the summer (March 25 to September 20), and lowered at sunset.

The red ensign should always be worn on the ensign staff at the stern of the boat.

Saluting by steamboats is not normally carried out in confined waters except when meeting Royal yachts and HM or foreign naval vessels. These should be saluted at all times.

A salute is made by lowering the ensign until its lower edge is approximately two-thirds down from the truck; it is held in this position until the vessel being saluted has dipped her ensign and started to hoist it again.

The ensign is then slowly raised making sure that the vessel being saluted is the first to complete the operation.

2. **The BURGEE**

The burgee is a triangular flag 9" or longer, having a distinctive design adopted by a yacht club or association and worn by the boat whose owner is a member.

The burgee should only be worn by a steam boat if the owner is on board or nearby. It may be worn day and night at sea, but when in harbour it should be hoisted and lowered at the same times as the ensign.

The burgee should be worn at the mainmast, or on the staff at the bows if there is no mast.

3. **The COURTESY ENSIGN**

When British vessels visit or anchor off a foreign port they should wear a small ensign of that country as token of courtesy.

Foreign ensigns are normally two thirds the length of the hoist.

The foreign ensign should be worn at the mainmast yardarm between 0800 and sunset.

If the vessel does not have a mainmast, the ensign should be worn above the burgee on the staff at the bows.

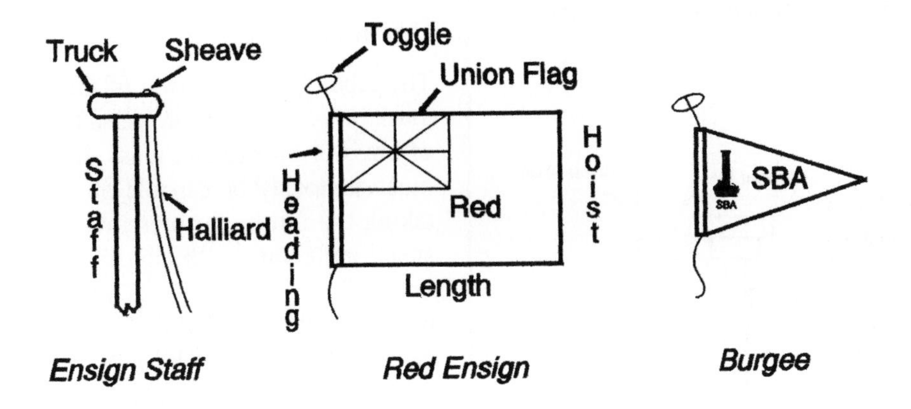

Ensign Staff *Red Ensign* *Burgee*

19. **The Water Level Gauge**

Purpose:

The water level gauge is used to show the amount of water in the boiler.

Principle:

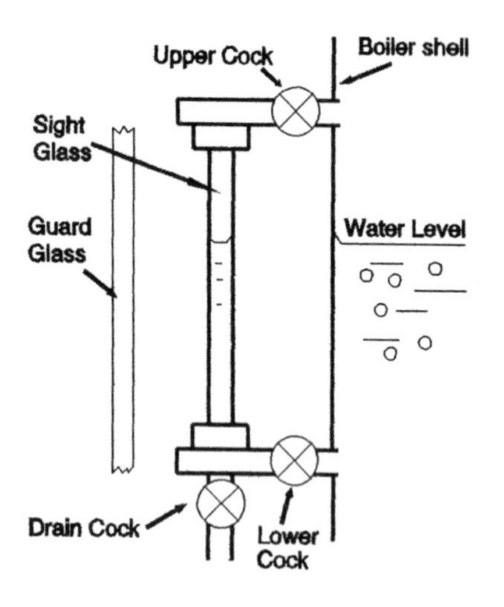

A transparent tube is connected to the boiler drum through two pipes, one above and one below the nominal working water level. The water level in the tube is thus the same as that in the boiler drum, whatever the pressure in the boiler may be. The connections are positioned by the boiler designer such that, if the water is visible anywhere in the gauge, the water level is satisfactory. Generally, the best level is about two-thirds of the way up.

Operation:

The tube is usually made of thick glass or quartz, or is an assembly of brass or bronze and glass. It must obviously be capable of taking the full boiler pressure, at steam temperature (though this is not really a problem - it is only in the last few years that the electricity authorities have abandoned their visual gauges, and they run at pressures around 2400 psi). The glass must be free of cracks or scratches and cleanly cut - no notches or spikes which cause weakness. It is good practice to replace the glass every so often as a matter of course - and always carry a spare.

A gauge glass breaking under pressure is a somewhat traumatic situation. To avoid or minimise the risk the glass must always be enclosed in a guard made of heavy (10 mm thick) glass or plastic. This both protects the glass from accidental damage and protects you from flying glass, steam and superheated water in the event of a fracture.

If the glass does fail, it must be possible to shut off the steam and water by means of isolating cocks. In an emergency, they can also be used as test cocks to check the water level when the glass is broken (ease them open and make sure that water comes out of one and steam out of the other). Sometimes separate test cocks (*try cocks*) are fitted to the boiler especially for this purpose.

The cocks, together with the gauge drain cock, are used to test the gauge for blockage at least every time steam is raised. Close the lower cock and open the drain; steam will blow through the upper connection and the gauge. Close the upper cock and open the lower; water blows through the lower connection; close the drain and open the upper and the gauge will operate. The water level should be continually moving slightly; if not check for blockage. (Sometimes the lower cock and the drain are combined in a three-way cock.)

If the level in the gauge rises when you start the engine or the safety valve blows, and drops when you stop, or if the gauge appears to be "streaming" inside, or if you are not quite sure where the water level is, your boiler is *priming*. This is usually caused be dirty water and is similar to the effect when you shake a bottle of lemonade (or champagne) and then release the pressure. The whole bottle (boiler) fills up with frothy bubbles which will make the whistle splutter and the engine bang. Drain down and put in clean water as soon as possible.

20. **GAUGE GLASS REPLACEMENT**

Don't be fooled by the sound appearance of your gauge glass. It tends to deteriorate on the inside and at the ends; a reduction of half the thickness in only two years is not unknown. The glass can also crystallize and lose strength without any outward signs. It is good practice to examine them every year and to replace them every other year without fail. Always destroy the one that you remove.

Gauge Glass Seals

It can be very difficult to find good quality gauge glass sealing rubbers these days. Viton or Silicone rubber 'O' rings, used in pairs, are an excellent substitute. Best used with a 0.010/0.015" interference fit on section, but they will also work well if compressed in the normal way with a gland follower.

21. GRP HULL FITTING OUT

If you are planning to fit out a fibreglass hull, it is necessary to take precautions against distortion while building. Do not forget the following golden rules:

(a) Set the keel horizontal with a spirit level checked in at least three positions along its length;

(b) With a straight edge across the stern, set the hull level with a spirit level. Repeat in three places equally spaced along the top edge of the hull;

(c) Set the beam of the hull to the desired dimension without stressing it. (Remember that the narrow canal locks are only 6'10" wide.)

(d) Recheck (b) when glassing in major bulkheads and lockers.

If you set the hull up correctly as above, you can use the spirit level with confidence throughout construction, and you will not suffer the shock of finding out that the hull is twisted when it is too late!

Fixings in GRP

If you are fixing timbers to a fibreglass hull, do not forget:

(a) To allow a generous clearance hole around the screws to stop surface crazing in the vicinity;

(b) Use a soft washer (nylon is ideal) or a strip of wood under the screw heads. This particularly applies to fittings passing through the hull, hot or cold.

22. MOORING HOOKS

When securing a mooring line to a hook there is no need to go through the laborious procedure of passing the end of the line through the eye several times. Simply bend the rope double at the position to be secured and pass the loop thus formed through the eye of the hook. Pull the loop sufficiently to pass the hook through it, then pull it back to tighten it round the eye. Once tightened it will be quite secure without further knots. However, if you want belt and braces, a loop in the free end can be further secured with a half-hitch round the lead. To undo, reverse the procedure by freeing the loop on the eye and pass the hook through it.

23. **HOTWELL OIL SEPARATOR**

There can be no doubt that direct oil lubrication in the steam improves the performance and lengthens the life of an engine. It must be the right oil such as 'Valvata' or 'Stuart Turner Special', but even then, a build-up of it in the boiler can spell disaster at worst or reduced efficiency at best. What can we do about it? There is only one answer, which is to provide a well designed hotwell with the following features:

(a) A settling tank with a diffused inlet near the top (capacity about ⅔" per lb/hr flow). Outlet at the bottom into:

(b) A separator with a feed passage up to the top, then constrained through a large square or round tube (entrance hole 0.9") set at 45° and 12" long. The tube to be packed tight with plastic drinking straws; water flow from top to bottom. Easy access to the straws is essential so that they can be washed with petrol when saturated with oil.

(c) Then into the final filter tank (capacity ¾" per lb/hr flow) which contains either: loosely packed old terry towelling (wherever cut, seal

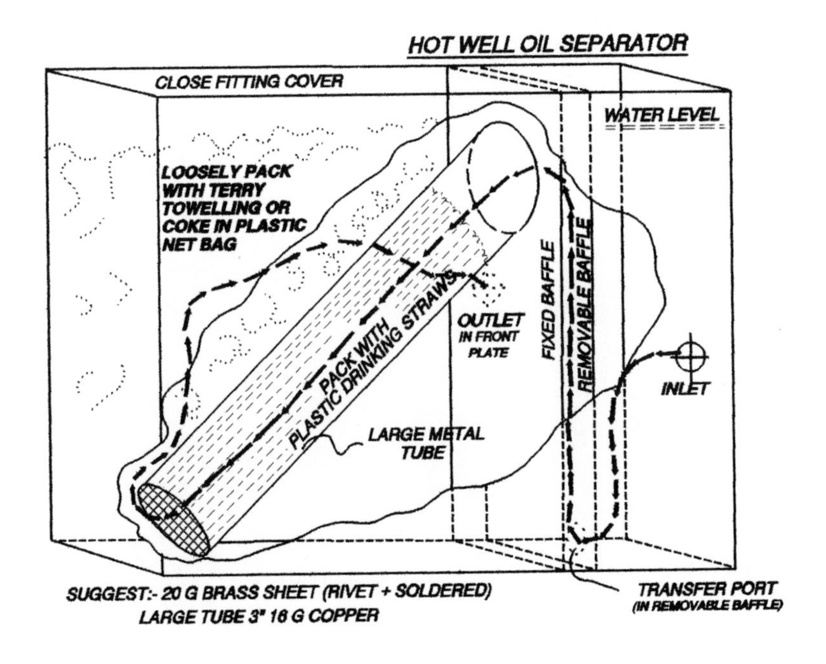

edge with rubber adhesive), or: a neatly fitting wire basket full of coke or Coalite. (This form is ideal for coal burners, the saturated filter bed being disposed of in the firebox from time to time.) Discharge connection halfway up and remote from the inlet.

For efficient operation, tank must be kept at least ¾ full.

All the above compartments are best in one sub-divided tank, but they may also be separated. Height is most important, also hand access for cleaning and removing filter elements. The ideal is a tall flat tank; example 18" tall, 20" wide and 4" thick (see illustration).

24. **HULLS**

Committee members and others are often asked: "How does one set about making a steamboat?" The answer is always "Join the SBA, read FUNNEL and come to meetings to see how other people have done it." Excellent advice which cannot be bettered, but not all that easy for a beginner to put into practice. In this and succeeding articles I want to try to cover the fundamental principles at a level suitable for someone who does not yet know the difference between a boiler and a bailer or between an inspector and an injector. Perhaps by the end, these differences will be a little clearer.

***KITTIWAKE**, A traditional Windermere launch*

The largest part of any steamboat is of course the boat itself, and usually the boat is the first thing decided on, although occasionally somebody may get an engine and then look for a hull to put it in. Any craft at all can be used as the basis for a steamer; SBA meetings have seen boats based on canoes, skiffs, sailing dinghies, speedboats, motor launches, electric launches, clinker, carvel, steel, plywood, cold-moulded, and virtually every type of boat and construction you can think of. (I can't offhand think of an inflatable one - any offers?) Your choice must depend on what you want and your resources. Consider firstly where you are going to keep it. If you have moorings or a boathouse on navigable water (lucky you!), then you have quite a lot of freedom as to size. If you want to keep it on a trailer in the garden, or want for various reasons to be able to move it around, there are practical limits. From experience, a boat which is going to be trailed regularly and launched from slipways should not be more than about 20 ft (6 m) long or weigh more than about

15 cwt (1700 lbs or 760 kg). If you want to carry it on a car top, it must obviously be much lighter and it must be possible to take the heavy parts (engine and boiler) out easily.

The second question is: how many people are going to ride on board? Obviously the minimum is one, and most boats of any type are more easily handled by two people (steamboating is a social activity, after all). If you want to carry more, will they be passengers or crew? Will they want to keep out of the rain or sparks under an awning or cabin? The best way of deciding how big a boat you need is to look at a few examples in FUNNEL. For example, the centre pages of FUNNEL 18 show four boats at Beaulieu - **LEO**, 12 ft, has two on board, **SIOUX**, 18 ft, has five, **BERYL**, 22 ft, has four in her (though according to the Index, she has seats for seven), and **MORVEN**, 20 ft, has seats for six. Other well known examples are **SOOTY** (11 ft - capacity two small ones), **SIRIUS 6** (a two man canoe) and **MUDLARK** (19 ft), whose maximum capacity has yet to be determined - see FUNNEL 27, front cover.

LIGHTNING, a Frolic 18 commercial glass fibre hull

A useful rule of thumb (which I have just invented) is 1 ft 6 in per person and 10 ft for the boat. However, some people need more space than others. Babies and elderly relatives tend to be more space-consuming than smallish children and able-bodied adults, while most boat owners consider it an achievement to make teenage children come at all. Always bear in mind that you can run into insurance and regulation problems if you take more than twelve people in addition to the crew.

How fast do you want to go? The speed you can push a boat along with a reasonable amount of power depends mainly on the length. If you want to go faster, a longer boat will generally be more rewarding than a bigger engine (see articles in FUNNELS 13 and 17). Examples of this are **SOOTY**, whose performance improved significantly when an extra foot or so was added to her length, and **SAUMAREZ V**, who also appears to run better after an extension of 3 ft. Unfortunately, there do not seem to have been any before-and-after tests done on these boats, and **SOOTY** has now been dismantled. However, in the 1984 Windermere speed trials (FUNNEL 42) **SAUMAREZ** investigated the effect of moving weight aft, thus putting the counter lower and effectively increasing the waterline length. The effect was an increase in speed over the measured kilometre from 4.9 knots to 5.4 knots.

This rule only applies to displacement (i.e. ordinary) boats; the rules governing speedboats which, like many sailing dinghies, can plane over the top of the water, and submarines are quite different. To estimate the speed potential of a boat, take the waterline length in feet, take its square root and multiply by 1.25, to get the speed in knots (if you are a purist and want the speed in miles/hour on fresh water, multiply by 1.44 instead. If you prefer Roman Catholic units, use the length in metres and multiply its square root by 4.2 to get the speed in km/hr.) Thus a 16 ft boat might be expected, with a suitable power plant, to make about:

$$1.25 \times 4 = 5 \text{ knots}$$

The **QUEEN MARY** (length about 900 ft) should in theory make about 37.5 knots, but in practice with big ships, the multiplying factor falls to about 1.00. Remember that many waters have speed limits, often around 5 to 10 miles/hour (canals 4 miles/hour).

Having chosen your size of boat, how about its shape, appearance and construction? Again, what do you want? If you want Edwardian elegance, either original or reproduced, the general proportions are already decided and a good deal of varnished wood is likely to be involved. If you want a cheap and reasonably rugged boat, fibreglass suggests itself. If you expect to operate a lot in very restricted waters such as canals, then choose steel or good solid oak.

Design of the underwater shape of a boat is a job for the expert, but above the waterline, shape has a lot of freedom. You can choose various shapes for the bow (the sharp end): straight vertical, curved backwards (perhaps the most common), or forwards (clipper) without affecting the performance in the water very much. The other end, the stern, however matters much more. It must provide support and protection for the propeller, a mounting for the rudder and often room for the steersman, without producing too much water resistance. The most common stern shapes are the transom, flat crossways and often vertical (e.g. the two boats on the right hand centre pages of FUNNEL 31) and the counter, a smoothly sloping overhang from below the water to above (e.g. **ALDEBARAN**, front cover of FUNNEL 36). A rather different shape is the canoe stern (similar to the bow, e.g. **LAUGHING WATER** in FUNNEL 37). Remember that it must be possible to get at the propeller to remove weed, rope or plastic bags which get entangled. With a transom this can often be done by leaning over the side; with a counter, either a bathing suit or a specially provided *weed hatch* is usually necessary.

The width (beam) and the depth (draught) of a boat usually follow by conventional proportions to the length for any given general type.

***SENTA**, a converted Flying Dutchman sailing dinghy hull*

There is scope for some variation. Remember there are practical and legal problems in towing trailers that are significantly wider than the car, and some waterways have bridges and locks of limited size. Shallow draught is generally an advantage on trailed boats and has few snags. The propeller may project below the lowest point of the boat and it is advisable to provide some protection. This can sometimes be provided by the rudder which is usually immediately behind the propeller.

Few of us are in the happy position of being able to specify our boat completely; a much more likely situation is going to be looking at a boat being offered and asking oneself: "Will that make a good steamboat?"

Several points come into the answer to this question. Firstly most steam boats are propeller driven; paddlers are a subject in themselves, and if you want to make a steam powered outboard, a jet propelled boat or one rowed by a steam robot, this article is not for you. So we will assume that you need a propeller shaft running from inside the boat to the outside. Is there one? Most ex-motor launches will have one. If not would it be reasonably easy to put one in? (Ask a boatbuilder.) If there is, is there room for a big enough propeller under the stern? Remember - steam boats have rather bigger propellers than motor boats for reasons I shall get round to in a later article, and it is essential that the top of the propeller is several inches below the surface of the water. Typical diameters for trailable steam launches are 11 to 25 inches.

Inside the boat is there room for the engine and boiler? Are there strong enough mountings (bearers) in position for them? For a given boat a steam plant is rather bulkier and maybe a bit heavier than a petrol or diesel engine would be. Typically, for a trailer boat a single cylinder engine needs about 1 ft square and a two cylinder about 2 ft by 1 ft. A boiler to match these might need a space as much as 2 ft wide and 3 ft long, plus an adequate working space near the fire door which is usually at the back, nearest to the engine. Since these components are heavy they must be near the centre of the boat. Space is also needed for water tanks - anything from 1 to 20 gallons depending on the type of installation, required range and quality of local supplies - and fuel, depending on the type and range required.

If the boiler is to be a vertical type, it will affect the stability of the boat. A boiler for a trailer boat weighs about the same as its owner, so try standing up in the boat where the boiler is to be. If you find yourself pointing head downwards the boat is not stable enough. Otherwise try to get a feel for how much the boat will rock when disturbed by waves, crew movement, etc. This is called the *tenderness* of the boat. Quite large movements may be quite safe in a well designed boat, although uncomfortable. Traditional steam launches are much more tender than modern flatter bottomed designs. Try to compare the behaviour of your chosen boat with others you meet at rallies, to get a feel for what is acceptable to you.

When a boat passes all these tests, you have the makings of a potential steamboat. The rest is up to you. Remember that all boats must be properly fitted out and maintained for the waters on which they will be used. Adequate mooring, anchoring, buoyancy, navigating and/or other types of nautical equipment will be needed. These are not the subject of this article; be guided by experienced boat owners and builders, and by rules, regulations and guidelines issued by navigation authorities. The only extra items of boat equipment needed specifically for a steamboat are fire extinguishers, an extra large ensign and an SBA burgee.

By the next issue I will expect all readers to have obtained and prepared their boats ready for the installation of steam plant.

25. **STEAM IMMERSION HEATER**

Although a Windermere kettle has great aesthetic appeal, it is very limited when it comes to fluids other than water. In a seaway, boiling water slopping about in a container fixed to the hull can be rather hazardous. A much safer substitute is a small stainless steel heating coil: ¼" OD, ⅛" ID tube is ideal. Make a flat coil from about two feet of tube, shaped to enter your kettle easily. It must be accessible for pans or the kettle with a hook to support the latter in order to avoid a steamed hand. Feed with live steam from the boiler via a stop-valve and discharge into the hotwell below the water level.

26. THE INJECTOR

Purpose:

The injector is a boiler feed pump with no moving parts, which works directly off the steam pressure.

Principle:

Boiler steam passes through a convergent-divergent passage, in

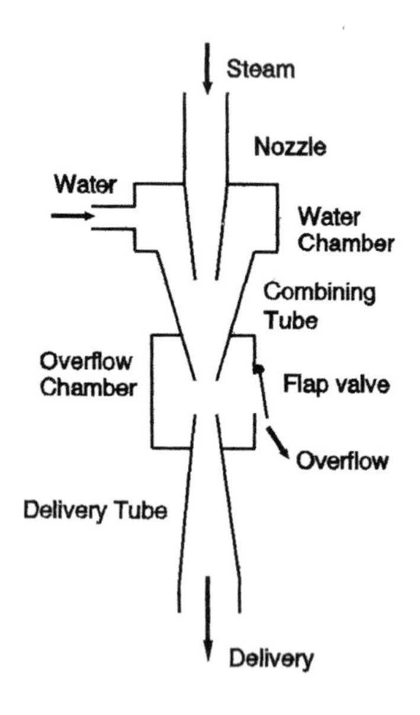

the process converting some of its temperature energy and much of its pressure to kinetic energy. The resulting very high speed (supersonic) flow is mixed with cold water, and immediately condenses. The warm water, which has a very much lower volume and higher density and is still moving fast, then passes through a divergent passage which slows it down almost to rest, at the same time increasing its pressure to a little above boiler pressure. It passes through a check valve into the boiler.

The apparent anomaly of being able to create a pressure higher than the supply pressure is explained by the conversion of heat energy, as well as pressure, to kinetic energy. The nozzle is, in fact, a form of heat engine.

Operation:

The principle of an injector's operation is not too difficult to understand, but the problems of making one that works reliably are often significant. The dimensions of the various nozzles are critical, and mainly found from experiment. A drain (overflow), with a non-return valve is fitted for use at start-up.

Injectors are notoriously fussy about installation. General rules, such as they are, are that they must be kept cold, supplied with cold water, have a long steam supply pipe and be as near the supply water level as possible (almost flooded, in fact). Many other rules, traditions and superstitions exist, so follow the maker's advice and ask people who seem to be able to use them. They will give contradictory advice, some of which may turn out to be helpful.

Starting an injector is half the battle. Again, most designs have their favourite sequence. A common one is:

(a) open the water control valve fully;

(b) open the steam valve fully - the overflow will start;

(c) close the water control slowly until the overflow stops.

The injector should now work, and may make a singing noise. If steam comes out of the overflow, it is too hot; turn everything off, cool the injector with cold water and start again.

Small injectors are very easily blocked. They must be fed with completely clean water, through a fine mesh strainer. They will not accept warm water - no feed heating allowed! They are difficult to clean due to the very narrow passages. Procedures such as boiling in vinegar are sometimes recommended. Never push anything solid through the nozzles, as this will scratch them and almost certainly stop them working completely.

The advantages of the injector over other feed pumps are obvious - small size and lack of mechanical complication. Properly installed they are very effective - railway locomotives used almost nothing else. Their disadvantages are: starting problems, inability to work before steam pressure has been raised and slightly lower thermodynamic efficiency due to effectively using live steam for feed water heating.

27. INSTALLATION

Condensers

In the last article, I did not manage to discuss condensers in any detail, so here goes.

The condenser cools the exhaust steam, turning it back to water. To do this, a good supply of cold water (or occasionally air) is needed. The most common and the simplest on small boats is the keel cooler (why do you want to cool your keel?) - a length of pipe outside the hull, close to the keel for protection. Inboard condensers usually need a separate pump to circulate the cooling water.

The condenser has two completely independent functions: to recover feed water for re-use and to improve efficiency. The latter arises because if you condense steam in a confined space, the pressure can fall to well below atmospheric pressure. If the confined space is at the outlet of the engine, you effectively increase the pressure difference by up to about 15 psi (in practice more like 10 psi), and so increase the power produced by your engine for the same boiler pressure. The first steam engines (called *atmospheric engines*) worked completely by this method - and their boiler pressure was practically zero.

The snag is that to get the water out of the condenser - which you have to do whether you intend to use it again or not - you need an extra pump. This is the extractor or *Air Pump* (so called because much of the time it is handling air which comes out of solution in the water, or gets in by mistake). it absorbs some of your extra power, but, because the water has a much lower volume than steam, there is a net gain in efficiency.

The disadvantages of condensing are extra complexity, the loss of the ability to 'puff' up the funnel to draw the fire and, if you re-use your water and use cylinder lubricating oil, you will have the additional problem of separating the oil to stop it getting into the boiler. Whether you want a condenser for either reason is up to you - on clean, fresh water (e.g. Windermere) there is not much advantage; at sea there is.

Pipework

The main power cycle needs pipework to carry the working fluid (water/steam) from the feed pump to the boiler (relatively cold water, but under pressure), from the boiler to the engine (hot, pressurized steam), from the engine to the condenser (fairly hot but low pressure steam), and from the condenser via the hotwell (tank) to the feed pump (cold low pressure water). All these have different needs.

Cold low pressure water is easy - anything will do. Plastic rubber, copper and steel are widely used and joints can be compression fittings, solder capillary, screw, jubilee clip, glue or whatever. The condenser pipework, though, needs to take negative (outside) pressure, and thin-walled flexible hose is liable to collapse and is therefore unsuitable.

Cold, high pressure water must have metallic or high pressure hose pipework. Domestic plumbing is not suitable. The check valve end of the feed pipe tends to get hot when not feeding, so that high temperature hose is advisable. For the same reason, soft solder should not generally be used. Although its melting point, around 200°C, corresponds to steam at over 200 psi, it is very weak at temperatures much above 100°C. With copper tube, either silver solder, brazing or high pressure compression fittings should be used.

The main steam pipe from boiler to engine should be either screwed steel or thick walled copper with silver soldered, brazed or high pressure compression fittings. High pressure, high temperature hose may be used if you have the necessary specialist know-how to install and maintain it.

The exhaust plumbing is relatively easy - domestic copper with capillary solder or compression fittings is perfectly satisfactory.

The sizes of pipe may be chosen by looking at the various ports on the pumps, boiler and engine. As a rough guide, most small installations will be happy with a ¼" to 5/16" bore on the water system and ½" to ¾" on the steam side. In general, it is better to err on the larger side (within reason). Pipe runs should be as short as is reasonably possible, avoiding sharp bends and constrictions. This applies particularly to the steam pipes - the speed corresponding to 50 lb/hr is about 0.7 ft/sec in a ¼" feed pipe, 45 ft/sec in a ½" 100 psi steam pipe and 273 ft/sec in a ½" atmospheric pressure exhaust pipe. At the latter speeds, sharp bends can give significant pressure losses.

Other pipework should follow the same sort of principles - consider always the temperature, pressure and speed of flow (and for gas or liquid fuel, chemical compatibility). In particular, make sure that the safety valve vent pipe is big enough. When I first fitted one to **SENTA**, I found that a ½" (domestic) pipe could not vent fast enough to lower the pressure, while a ¾" one could.

Plumbing

There is no real problem in plumbing a simple non-condensing system with no auxiliaries. But when pipes start to branch and join, you must take care.

Every pump should have its own delivery valve internally, but it is wise to fit an extra non-return valve to each of the various deliveries, close to where they join. This prevents a stuck valve in one of them releasing the pressure from others. The suction side will be all right so long as the inlets are 'flooded' - below hot-well water level. All intakes from the hot-well and all other tanks, the bilge or the sea, should be slightly above the bottom and fitted with a gauze strainer. I made a very satisfactory one out of a nylon coffee strainer from Woolworths. Many injectors like to be flooded, or almost so. Consult the supplier about plumbing injectors - breeds differ, and are particular.

Every steam outlet from the boiler, except the safety valve, should be fitted with a stop-valve as close to the boiler as possible. If there is a manifold supplying several auxiliaries from one boiler outlet, each outlet branch should have its own stop-valve. Many people also fit a stop valve between the check valve and the boiler.

A whistle will only work when it is warm. Blowing a cold whistle results in a spluttering noise and a shower of warm water, sometimes followed by a rather wet toot. Three ways of keeping the whistle dry are used: mount it direct on the boiler drum, run the whistle pipe up inside the funnel, or keep the whistle valve slightly open so that there is a very small but continuous flow of steam through it. Fitting a steam/water separator close to the whistle may also help.

Lagging

Steam is hot. To keep it hot, and stop it heating things it shouldn't (such as people), lagging is needed. For efficiency, the boiler, main engine steam pipe and engine cylinders need lagging. For safety, exhaust pipes and all other hot surfaces should be lagged. Lagging is simply thermal insulation, with something to hold it on and make it weatherproof. Commercial laggings are various sorts of mineral fibres (including glass); asbestos is out of favour nowadays. I have found fibreglass loft insulation from a DIY shop very satisfactory on the boiler. Fibreglass strip for winding round hot water pipes is satisfactory on the steam pipe, but difficult to keep in place. Split circular foam rubber pipe insulation, held on with insulating tape is fine on the exhaust, but tends to melt on the main steam pipe. This year I have tried a single layer of woven fibreglass tape (about 3 mm thick) with the foam rubber over the top, which seems all right.

The funnel needs to be insulated to stop the paint burning off. (Even stove enamelling may burn off.) This is usually done with an air space - a large outer false funnel is fitted over the inner flue, with a minimum number of spacers holding them apart.

Miscellaneous Points

Many modern materials are far superior to traditional materials. (Traditionalists of a nervous disposition who wish to read further may like to ensure a supply of liquid moral support.) Edwardian boatbuilders did not use plastic, polyurethane, stainless steel or aluminium - they did not have the option. We have. Building materials available for DIY use are perfectly adequate for use on small boats in non-commercial operation. There is no need to buy specialist boat-building paints or caulking compounds - outdoor gloss paint and bath-tub (or window frame) sealant have had much more research put into them than tar and oakum, and are much more durable and easier to use. PTFE thread tape works just as well as white lead for sealing pipe threads even for steam (I know - I use it), and you can undo it again. A smear of high temperature graphite or molybdenum grease works wonders for tight taper cocks, whilst a good thick gear oil will stay in your main bearings just as long as specialist steam oil. Troublesome conical pipe fittings can be cured with 'Stag' or 'Hermetite' jointing (though a good metal-to-metal joint is really preferable). Boiler and cylinder gaskets are usually happy with a smear of graphite and oil.

28. **LAGGING**

In order to achieve a professional appearance on your steam plant, neat lagging is essential. One way of doing this is to lag with mineral wool which in turn is wrapped with plaster of paris impregnated medical bandage. This is readily obtainable from your chemist. It is simply soaked in water before application and can be smoothed to a fine finish by hand. A final coat of emulsion when dry will waterproof it and give it protection and a good appearance.

29. LATHE TURNING TIPS

Lathe Chatter

Chatter in a finishing cut with a broad tool in the lathe or with a countersink cutter can be very exasperating. It is usually a consequence of too high a cutting speed. Low speeds for finishing cuts is one answer. Another is to turn the chuck or cutter slowly by hand for the final skim to size. This trick is also handy for getting rid of chatter once it has occurred.

Interrupted cuts

There is often a need for an interrupted cut on the lathe, when turning a casting with a boss on one side or producing the recess in the lip of a whistle for example. This can be done by moving the chuck through the required arc by hand with the chuck key whilst feeding the tool in the normal way. The feeds will have to be small to prevent digging in, but good speeds can be achieved by experiment.

30. **LAYING UP YOUR BOILER**

Boilers frequently suffer more damage from corrosion while standing than they do when they are at work. Effective laying-up is well worth the time and trouble spent. There are two aspects of the operation to consider, the fire side and the water side.

Let us first consider the fire side. All fuels contain a proportion of sulphur and much of this remains in the products of combustion, namely: ash and soot. With the introduction of moisture the sulphur forms sulphuric acid - wicked stuff when in contact with metal. If the boiler can be kept dry there is no problem, but any idle boiler will sooner or later become damp, so it is imperative that the ash and soot are completely removed. A boiler left standing with water therein will quickly sweat - that is, condensation will take place on the cool surfaces - and this will produce more than just dampness, quite substantial amounts of water will collect eventually and the more water present, the more sulphuric acid may be formed.

As regards the water side, there are two effective ways of laying a boiler up, both taking cognisance of one fact common to both. Corrosion depends on two features, moisture and oxygen. Expel either one and corrosion cannot take place.

Short term lay-up, expel the air

Vent the boiler at the highest point and fill it right up with water. The oxygen which is in the air is driven right off with the air and cannot then cause corrosion inside the boiler. The oxygen dissolved in the water is very little and corrosion will be negligible. Chemical additives can be used to absorb this oxygen if desired. A boiler, laid-up in this manner, however, is bound to sweat and corrosion will readily take place on the fire side.

Long term lay-up, expel the moisture

Empty the boiler and dry the fire side thoroughly; a gentle heat can be used for this, an electric fire for instance. When all the moisture that can be removed physically has been removed, place trays of slaked lime wherever the type of boiler allows and seal the boiler up again as for steaming. The lime will absorb any humidity in the boiler and create a dry atmosphere in which corrosion cannot take place. Further admittance of atmospheric moisture is impossible of course because the boiler has been hermetically sealed.

In this case, under reasonable conditions, the fire side can also be kept dry, as the condensation problem is so diminished as to be manageable.

In conclusion it should be pointed out that the worst treatment a boiler can be given is to leave it after steaming with a working level of water in it and ash and soot lying in and about the firebox and flues.

31. **OIL FIRED**

The following piece of poetry on the burning of fuel oil should be committed to memory by every junior engineer:

Set the burners open wide
Do not touch the valve at side
Keep the pressure on the pump
And up the bally steam will jump.
If the smoke is black and thick,
Open up the fans a bit;
If the smoke is thick and white,
To slow the fans will be quite right;
For when sufficient air is given,
No smoke ascendeth up to Heaven.
If the jets refuse to squirt,
Assume the cause is due to dirt;
Should the flame be short and white,
You have combustion clear and bright;
But should the flame be yellow and long,
Combustion is entirely wrong.
A wise man to his heater sees
And keeps it at ten score degrees;
To have it more is not quite wise,
Because the oil may carbonize.
A little lower has been found
To give as good results all round.
If the filters are kept clean,
No rise in pressure will be seen;
But should the pump kick up a ruction,
There's likely air within the suction.
The pressure governs the supply -
So do not keep it very high.
If these instructions you will follow,
You'll beat the other fellow hollow!

32. **PASSENGERS**

Another season of SBA rallies is upon us and, with the arrival of new passengers, there is the usual shy revelation from some people - and not always the ladies - that they know nothing about boats and are not at all sure what is expected of them as passengers. Some even go so far as to wonder whether owners resent their presence. Although something in the form of a *Guide for Passengers* has appeared in FUNNEL before, perhaps a few words for the benefit of more recent members might prove helpful, even reassuring.

First, do be assured that passengers are most welcome. The SBA wants to help members gain experience and a good way to do this is to see a steam plant in action and, hopefully, doing the job it was built to do. There is also the chance to ask questions on the spot of the person who probably built the engine or at least runs and maintains the plant. If the passenger does not already talk the language, it's one way to start.

That said, it must also be pointed out that owners put a lot of hard work into their boats and this is not done with the sole object of carrying passengers at rallies. In other words, boats must not be regarded in any way as hire craft. The owner may be feeling his way with the engine, or a problem may develop - no-one is immune. He will always, however, want to share his experience and joy in steam boating with passengers so it does help if they have some idea of what is expected of them. So here are some points to watch.

Coming on Board

Do wait until you are actually invited aboard. The skipper and crew have many jobs to do before the boat is ready to leave, and in most boats these cannot be done with any ease if one has to step over passengers. This may not apply to a few large boats but it does to those of more modest size.

Trimming the Ship

Small boats are easily unbalanced by badly distributed weight. You are a weight. If you have a companion, don't assume that you can just sit side by side and be 'out of the way'. This in itself could make the boat very lop-sided; one each side is usually better. Ask the skipper where to sit, then it is his responsibility. If you move about in the boat, just do it gently, keeping the idea of balance in mind.

Luggage

You should be self-sufficient and bring any food you may need and, of course, waterproofs. But please keep any luggage to an absolute minimum. Space is always at a premium in the boats and hearts will definitely sink if you appear with mountains of baggage. While on the subject, when you leave the boat for the lunch-stop, do take your luggage with you. There are several reasons for this: the skipper and crew need space to get at their own provisions if they are having a picnic and there are usually maintenance jobs to be done - like refuelling or clearing clinker - or even some adjustments. These are easier to do quickly if your luggage has gone, especially since essential equipment and tools are often stored underneath seats - exactly where extra luggage is likely to be stowed. Of course on bigger boats the owner may not mind at all and will invite you to leave your gear - but it all helps if you show an awareness of his needs and make it clear that you are prepared to remove it. Enough of that ....

Shoes

This one is so important that perhaps it should have come at the beginning. Soft shoes with non-slip soles are essential. Safety is a prime consideration here. Boat decks can be very slippery when wet. While a non-slip sole is no substitute for taking care, it will certainly help you to be more sure-footed when climbing in and out of a boat or in crossing from one boat to another when they are moored. Another important reason for this instruction about shoes is that many boats have beautiful varnish work which has taken the owner much long and careful work to achieve. Imagine how he will feel if people try to come on board with hard shoes and scratch or kick the surface, even accidentally. Soft shoes should prevent this sort of damage (*soft* shoes means **not** leather soles, or even hard rubber. Someone once turned up in walking boots with cleated soles and claimed to be wearing soft shoes!)

A Helping Hand?

There is no harm in offering to help, but you may be taken up on it. You could be involved in cleaning the brasswork! Occasions when you are most likely to be useful are when mooring or going through locks and there is some rope handling to be done. Ask for instructions if you don't know what to do and remember the golden rule - **never** get your fingers caught in a rope. When the rope takes the strain, it will trap your fingers and it will be impossible to release them quickly. Incredibly painful at best.

When mooring in locks you may be asked to "fend off". This means taking appropriate action to prevent the boats touching each other or a wall and thus causing damage (perhaps a bruise on that precious varnish work!). It is not difficult to fend off and doesn't usually require immense strength. However, there are two possible dangers: fingers can become trapped between two boats, so can an arm. So keep fingers and arms well clear. Don't go in for heroics and "hold on at all costs": you are not helping anyone if you fall in or even injure yourself.

Mind that Child!

If you bring a child, **you** must be in charge. The child should wear a life jacket and not be allowed to rush about. Jetties and banks can be slippery. There are ropes and gear to trip over and probably steamboaters lugging fuel and other things about. Remember too, that steamboats are not like rowing boats on a park lake; they have engines and pipework which can be very hot. Children and adults should keep this in mind when moving about on a boat - and take care.

The warning about fingers being trapped between boats obviously applies equally to children. Make sure they do not have hands and arms hanging over the sides if there is any chance of another boat coming alongside.

If you can be aware of these points, it will go a long way towards ensuring that you and the boats' crews have an enjoyable trip together. So: "Welcome Aboard!"

33. THE PRESSURE GAUGE

Purpose:

This gauge is used to show the pressure of the steam in the boiler or elsewhere such as between the cylinders of a compound engine. Often, pressure gauges are also used to show the pressure of oil fuel, feed water or other body fluids in a steamboat. A very similar device, the *vacuum gauge* is used to measure the pressure in the condenser.

Principle:

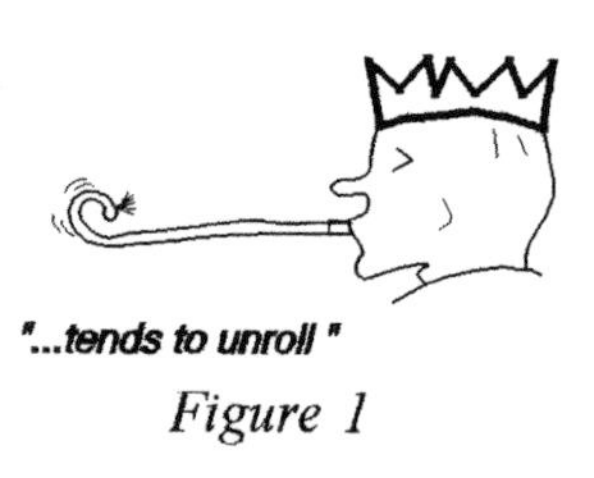

Figure 1

If a bent flattened tube is blown into, it tends to unroll (figure 1). The type of gauge usually used on steamboats, the *Bourdon Gauge* works on the above principle. The flattened steel tube is curved into a semi-circle. When pressurized, it tends to straighten out, and a link mechanism transfers this motion to the indicator needle (figure 2).

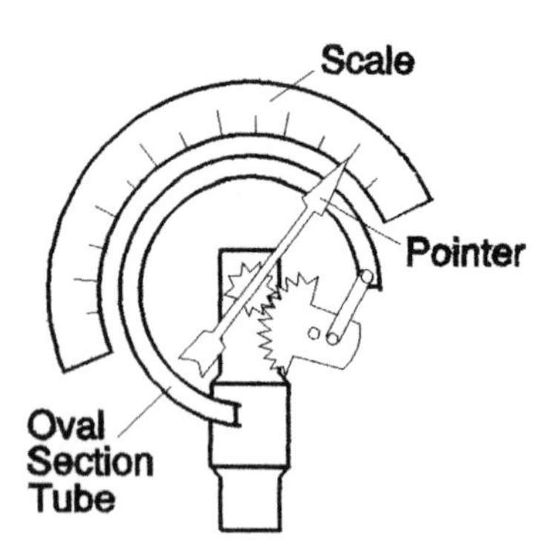

Figure 2: The Bourdon Gauge

Operation:

Pressure and vacuum gauges should be mounted vertically, with the connecting tube at the bottom. If used on steam, they must have a *wet bend*, an unlagged loop of tube whose purpose is to condense any steam before it arrives at the gauge. Gauges do not mind steam so long as it is hot, but they do not like water in their innards. Sometimes an isolating cock is fitted near the gauge to prevent water getting into it at shut-down. This can be a hazard, though, if you forget to open it.

The main boiler gauge calibration will be checked by the boiler inspector using a standard gauge. He (she) will not mind too much if it reads high, but will not allow under-reading.

34. **PROPANE FIRING**

SBA member Robert Cox has most kindly followed Dr S Pereira's suggestion at the AGM that some of the technical aspects of using propane gas as a fuel for steam boats should be investigated as part of our general concern with codes of practice in respect of boilers. he contacted Jonathan Barker, the Calor Gas group's liaison man, who was good enough to supply a list of regional technical Officers who would be the people to contact with technical problems if one were contemplating using Calor propane for boiler firing.

Mr Cox also mentions a scheme inaugurated by a boat hire firm on the Broads to use propane as a fuel for IC engines in hire boats. Should this prove successful it could spread to other waterways: this would lead to the provision of fuelling points ashore and the use of fixed horizontal tanks on board. This would be very useful for propane fired steam boats, greatly simplifying design and easing aesthetic problems involved in installing gas containers, removing the difficulty of obtaining bulk gas supplies and presumably allowing the use of liquid gas off-take with an external heated vapouriser, thus getting rid of the problem of pressure loss due to refrigeration of the container. We will endeavour to provide progress reports on this trial scheme; meanwhile Mr Cox has kindly offered to help anyone who would like to know more about the scheme, or indeed anyone who is considering using Calor gas as a steam boat fuel.

Finally, Mr Cox has brought to our attention BS 5482 Part 3 1979, entitled *Code of practice for Domestic Butane and Propane Gas-burning Installations in Boats, Yachts and other vessels*. This is a lengthy publication going into some detail, but the British Standards Institution have kindly given permission for us to quote one or two of the more directly relevant passages in order to give a little food for thought to existing or prospective gas users. (Those with boats registered on the Thames will find that the Thames Conservancy Division's requirements for gas installations as shown in the Launch Digest are largely based on the BS specifications.)

BS 5482: Part3: 1979 (Extract)

(Words in brackets represent additions or summarised passages.)

4. **Materials**

4.1 Pipework materials.

4.1.1 Recommended. The following materials are recommended for general use for installation pipework:
a) Solid drawn copper tube used with copper or copper alloy fittings.
b) Stainless steel tube and appropriate compression or screwed fittings.

4.1.2 Not recommended. The following materials are not recommended for general use for installation pipework for general use for the reasons shown:
a) Aluminium; - corrosion and low melting point.
b) Composition and lead; - creep.
c) Brass tubing; - subject to seasonal cracking.
d) Steel tubing; - corrosion.
e) Plastics; - low melting point and low temperature embrittlement.

(Where flexible hose is used, it should comply with the requirements for type 2 of BS 3212: 1975 . . . . provided with integral threaded metallic ends . . . .) (Hose supplied by Calor companies.)

5. **Components**

Components should comply with the relevant British Standards . . . (or) . . . should be of standard types recommended by manufacturers or wholesale gas distributors.

6. **Selection of appliances**

6.1 General. Appliances should normally comply with the requirements of the relevant British Standards, in particular BS 5258.

6.2 Selection of water heaters.
d) A water heater should . . . (be) . . . fitted with a flame failure device arranged to shut off the main and pilot gas supplies in the event of flame failure.

7. **Basic layout of supply system**

Layout should be such that the length of pipe from the cylinder to the highest rated appliances is as short as possible. All pipe runs should be made as short as practicable . . . and carried as high as possible in the vessel. They should not run through bilges.

9. **Installation design considerations**

9.1 General. Wherever possible . . . (propane) . . . cylinders should be stowed on the open deck or in a deck compartment or locker . . . (which) . . . should not be used for stowage of any equipment other than (propane) cylinders and pressure regulators. Unconnected or reserve cylinders should be stowed similarly . . . (and) . . .valves should be kept closed when . . . not in use and . . . (when) . . . empty.

9.4 Construction of cylinder lockers and compartments.
a) Cylinders should be secured in an upright position . . .
b) A locker . . . should be vapour-tight to the hull interior and openable only from the top (except a deck locker).
c) The materials used in the construction of a locker . . . should have a fire resistance of 30 minutes. (The Thames conservancy Division require a minimum of 20 wg metal with welded or brazed seams, or a self-quenching glassfibre moulding of not less than 4 oz material - approximately ⅛" thick.)

The locker . . . should be ventilated at low and high level to outside the hull. The low level vent pipe should be from the locker bottom above the deepest loaded water-line. Vent pipes should be of not less than 13 mm internal diameter for cylinders having a combined capacity of up to 15 kg, but they should be enlarged pro-rata where additional gas is carried.
c) The locker . . . should be designed to hold both the cylinders and the associated regulator equipment. The supply from the locker should be by fixed pipework from a suitable bulkhead fitting. (Vulnerable pipework should be suitably protected.)

15. **Gas detection**

Suitable means of detecting the leakage of gas should preferably be provided in each compartment containing a gas-consuming appliance and where this is a detector, it should be generally securely fixed in the lower part of the compartment in the vicinity of the gas-consuming appliance.

16. **Installation of unions and joints**

16.1 All unions and joints should be readily accessible for visual inspection. Connections . . . should be made only with pipe fittings. Soldered joints are not acceptable.

The BS specification goes on to describe methods of testing installations using manometers and compressed air etc. (For a single pipe installation to a steam boiler burner a simple method is to test with a strong soap solution such as undiluted washing-up liquid poured over the joints with the system pressurised.)

35. **PROPANE PRECAUTIONS**

It has been brought to the attention of the SBA committee that certain vessels have been at rallies using propane as a fuel in which the installation leaves something to be desired from the point of view of safety.

The committee, as stated previously, is anxious not to become involved in further excursions into the field of legislation, nor does it wish to become involved in a lengthy debate about the levels of risk or likely consequences of gas explosions. Suffice it to say that there is a definite potential for an unpleasant accident if propane is not used properly.

We have decided therefore to monitor the situation: that is to keep a benign eye on the installations in boats attending rallies, whilst seeking further technical advice from the relevant sections of the LPG industry with special reference to the peculiar problems of storing and using propane in a steam launch.

It seems reasonable therefore, at this juncture, to give a brief review of the considerations which should be taken into account with such installations.

The advantages of propane gas as a fuel for steam boilers have been well catalogued by Scott Pereira in FUNNEL 43. They can be summarised as 'the four Cs': **C**leanliness, **C**onvenience, **C**ontrollability and **C**alorific value - in many respects the ideal fuel, particularly for the medium sized trailable steam boat. The price to be paid for this "wonder fuel", apart from the monetary outlay, lies in the degree of responsibility required from the user in terms of the care he must take in installing and using the necessary equipment.

The danger is simply stated: propane gas is heavier than air and will therefore collect in the bottom of sealed structures such as boat hulls if leaked. It forms an explosive mixture with air at relatively low concentrations.

The problem with gas fired steam launches lies mainly in the particular way in which the fuel is employed compared with the cooking installation of, say, a motor cruiser. First of all, a lot of it is consumed; in most installations this means frequent changes of cylinder - with attendant leakage risks and wear on components. Secondly, the installation will be relatively complex and more vulnerable to damage than a short fixed pipe run to the back of a cooker. Thirdly, the boiler with its fire will of necessity be set low in the boat where an explosive mixture is likely to form.

The solution to these problems lies in the correct design and construction of the installation and in a few sensible precautions in its use. Such a code of practice exists in the form of BS 5482 (part 3) 1979, which is summarised in the Thames Conservancy Regulations as published in the *Launch Digest* given to the owners of all Thames registered craft. These requirements formed the basis of an article in FUNNEL 19 on the use of LPG in steamboats, but as many members will not possess that issue, they will be repeated hereinafter as a guide to the standard we would expect to see in SBA boats being used in public places. Remember, it would be just as difficult to explain to the authorities and to the insurance company why your propane plant did not comply with these recommendations following an accident as it would to explain away an untested and uncertified boiler which had exploded.

What is *not* wanted is: a gas cylinder standing exposed on the floor of a boat (covered by an old blanket when the lock-keeper is nearby), connected by an unprotected rubber hose (like the old school bunsen) which runs across the floor plates where tools, feet and beer cans vie for space, to a burner designed for town gas and fitted only with a simple tap.

What *is* wanted:

Bottle stowage:

Each bottle, whether in use or not, should be stored in an upright position in a locker which is vapour-tight to the hull interior and accessible only from the top. This would be of fire resistant material - e.g. a minimum 20 swg metal, welded or brazed seams, or a moulding of at least 4 oz fire resistant GRP - ventilated at the top and bottom to outside the hull above the maximum load water line - i.e. the bottom of the locker must be above the water line. This creates design problems for many small steamers owing to the height of the bottles. The idea is that any leaked gas should drain away overside and not be allowed to accumulate in the bottom of the locker itself. A strictly unofficial solution might be to ensure that any locker bottoms below this level are kept flooded or to make a moulding in the locker bottom up to the vent level using for example fire resistant polyurethane foam. This could be formed around a sample bottle treated with a suitable releasing agent. If any 'official' solution is forthcoming we will let you know.

The vent pipes themselves should be a minimum of 13 mm ID for a 15 kg bottle. The regulator should be contained within the locker and the delivery pipe should pass through a suitable leak-proof bulkhead fitting.

Pipework:

This should be of either solid drawn copper or stainless steel tube - such as that supplied by Calor - and not mild steel, aluminium, brass or plastic. It should be carried in a conduit if vulnerable to damage and generally kept as high as possible. Joints should be kept to a minimum, be outside any conduit and be of approved compression or screwed type. they should be accessible to visual inspection and periodic testing. (Washing up liquid is a good leak detector.) Short lengths of flexible hose, of the reinforced Calor variety, can be employed where not liable to damage or excess heat.

The Burner:

This, together with any regulators, taps, valves, etc. should comply with the BS. The simplest way is to consult your Calor or other commercial dealer. All burners should have a flame-failure shut-off valve as should pilot lights if fitted. These simple devices require no external power and are operated by a small sensor in the flame. The operator merely has to hold down a button for a few seconds on lighting up. The BS also recommends the use of gas detectors, but these are notoriously unreliable in small craft and require electrical power. A more useful investment would be a bilge scavenging pump driven either from its own power source or off the prop shaft, particularly if the whole plant were to be enclosed between gas-tight bulkheads as would ideally be the case.

Such an installation, if properly constructed and regularly checked, should be perfectly safe. The user must of course operate it sensibly and take simple precautions - for example, that valves are turned off when changing bottles and that this is not done in crowded surroundings such as locks where people might be smoking. Is this is done we should avoid finding out the hard way the exact effects of exploding propane-air mixtures and at the same time preclude the nausea of legislation.

36. PROPULSION

Quite simply, the engine turns the shaft, which turns the propeller, which pushes the boat. So all you need to do is to put in a shaft with a suitable prop at one end and a suitable engine on the other. So what is "suitable"?

The Propeller

To start at the stern, the propeller converts the rotary power of the engine to propulsive thrust. It does this in much the same way as a screw jack, but because water is not rigid, some of it gets pushed backwards - the wake or slipstream. This has energy which came from the engine - and this is a *Bad Thing*. Theory states that the thrust depends on the slip stream speed, but the wasted energy depends on the speed squared. So a large diameter with a low slip stream speed will waste less energy than a small one with a high slip stream speed. This applies to all sorts of propulsion which act on the water directly (but not to sailing or towing). Paddle wheels are better from this point of view than screw propellers, which is one reason why they were popular in the early days of steam. Similarly, eight hefty young men generating probably two or three horsepower, but using oars, can get a 70 ft boat from Putney to Mortlake in the same time as various escort boats putting tens of horsepower into propellers.

We thus should choose the largest diameter propeller possible (within reason) and run it slowly, to produce the right thrust without wasting too much power. What else must we know? Firstly, the number of blades: two, three or four are usual, with three the most common. In general, more blades transmit more power for the same speed and diameter; if you are a bit low on size, then you might try to compensate by using four blades rather than three. If you are buying a propeller, availability probably decides the number of blades. If you want to try to make your own, try to copy one on another boat as closely as possible. Secondly, the pitch, which is the angle the blades work are set at. If they are almost flat, viewed sideways on, the pitch is short or *fine*. If they are almost in line with the shaft, the pitch is long or *coarse*. The actual pitch measurement is the distance forward the propeller would (ideally) move if rotated once. Choice of pitch is an experimental art; most steamboat propellers have a pitch between 1 and 2 times the diameter - see the report on the Windermere speed trials in FUNNEL 42. A value of 1.5 is typical. A fine-lined hull will accept a coarser pitch than a short, wide hull, and a finer pitch is generally preferable in a sea boat which has to push against waves. There are some interesting, if not easily explained, results in FUNNEL 41, comparing the performance of different propellers on the same boat, **ELIDIR**. Lastly, we must choose the *hand* of our propeller. This is the same as for any screw thread: facing forward, a right-handed propeller will turn clockwise to go ahead and a left-handed one anti-clockwise.

A steamboat usually has a rather longer pitch than a motor boat. This is because petrol and diesel engines usually run faster and are more powerful than steam engines. A Stuart Turner 'Cygnet' engine is rated at about 1.5 HP at 800 revolutions per minute (rpm), while a petrol engine of the same cylinder dimensions (about 130 cc) might be expected to run at about 4000 rpm and develop about 7 HP. A finer pitch is thus appropriate, and the power lost due to the smaller diameter is more easily spared. Ignorant propeller merchants tend to look askance when asked for coarse propellers, but can usually get them if they try. In desperation, it has been known for the pitch to be increased by using a large wrench, or by cutting down a large diameter propeller to increase the pitch/diameter ratio. Such methods are best avoided unless you are very confident.

Speed of Rotation

To find out how fast to rotate your propeller, divide the boat speed (in mph) by the pitch in inches, and multiply by 1056. This gives the ideal speed in rpm. Unfortunately - it's wrong! In Engineering this sort of situation is often handled by introducing a 'Fiddle Factor', which converts the ideal answer to the correct one. In this case the factor is known as the *slip* (not to be confused with *slip-stream*). The article in FUNNEL 42 referred to above suggests slip values of 0.3 to 0.4. To get the required prop speed, subtract the slip from 1.0 and divide into the ideal prop speed. For example: if you have a 20" pitch prop with an estimated slip of 0.3 and want to go at 5 mph, the ideal prop speed is

$$\frac{5 \times 1056}{20} = 264 \text{ rpm}$$

and the actual, required prop speed is

$$\frac{264}{1.0 - 0.3} = 377 \text{ rpm.}$$

(In his chapter in Mitchell's *The Steam Launch*, Bill Durham suggests a slip of 0.15 to 0.25. It may be that at our SBA speed trials boats were running rather inefficiently because they were deliberately working at their limits rather than at normal cruising speed.)

The Shaft

The propeller is fitted on the shaft which passes through the hull of the boat. The shaft has to be held in such a way that it can rotate (obviously) and also to take the thrust of the prop and transfer it to the hull of the boat. Where the shaft emerges into the boat there must be a seal or *gland* to prevent water coming in. This gland is relatively easy to look after as it has very little pressure to support and a bit of leakage does not matter (and may even be a good thing). There is an article on gland packing on FUNNEL 17.

To take the shaft weight and generally keep it in the right place, two bearings are needed. The outer one, near the prop, may be mounted on the back of the *skeg* (the rearward extension of the keel) or on a special bracket under the counter. This bearing is usually water-lubricated and traditionally was made of a very hard wood (lignum vitae); nowadays it is normally rubber or plastic. The inner bearing may be a similar one, just behind the gland, or may be inside the boat, when it will be oil or grease lubricated. In this case it may be combined with a *thrust bearing*.

The thrust bearing may be anywhere on the shaft inside the boat, but is best fitted as near the gland as practical, to keep it out of the way. The thrust in a small steamboat is quite low - a few tens of pounds is typical - so the design of the thrust bearing presents no problems. A sealed ball race is satisfactory as it has low friction and, being grease lubricated, is effectively maintenance free. There are many suitable types in the catalogues; a deep-groove bearing will be quite satisfactory in most cases, or a specifically designed thrust bearing may be used. Remember to fit it the right way round, and make some provision for reversing.

Occasionally, the thrust bearing is incorporated into the engine, but this is not a very good idea; it is part of the propeller gear and should remain with it.

The Engine

The propeller shaft is driven by the engine, which is the next thing to specify. Clearly the power of the engine depends on how big the boat is and, to a lesser extent, on the required speed. Bill Durham (mentioned above) suggests a power of 1 to 3 HP per ton, to give a speed ratio (speed in knots divided by the square root of the waterline length in feet) of between 1.0 and 1.2. It is reasonable to be at the lower end of this if you know you are only going to work in calm water and good weather; otherwise it is better to err on the safe side.

Another approach is to calculate the horsepower the propeller you have chosen can absorb. In FUNNEL 14 there is a chart on page 47 and a table on page 48 for doing this.

Example: If you have a 14" diameter by 20" pitch prop, going at 377 rpm (as calculated above), you first use the chart to give the power for a 14" by 14" prop as 0.37 HP. Then, the table says that for a pitch/diameter ratio of 1.43 (20 divided by 14) the power should be multiplied by 2.25, giving 0.83 HP. A propeller of this size might be used on a boat up to about half a ton, giving around 2 HP per ton.

37. **PROPELLER MAINTENANCE**

Warts on the Propeller

For the first time **SAUMAREZ** has spent most of the year on a mooring on the Avon and has been subject to the ravages of marine growth. Anti-fouling looked after the hull very effectively and I thought that all was well until some days after snugging her down in her newly-built boat shelter for the winter. When getting ready to tackle some damp patches in the varnish work I noticed what looked like twenty or more bright green warts on her propeller. I quickly rubbed them off with fine abrasive paper only to find that each one was sitting over a pit $\frac{1}{6}$ inch deep and ⅛ inch in diameter. This discovery took me back many years to two problems experienced when servicing sea-going ships.

The first related to condenser packing failure encountered in a ship trading in the Red Sea. Leakage of seawater through the tube plate was traced to what looked like a hacksaw cut right through a ferrule and tube end. Luckily the culprit was discovered on another tube end just starting its destructive work. It was a string-like weed which had been drawn into two tubes by the flow. Tests showed that in decomposing the weed was producing a strong acid which its spongy structure held against the metal thus concentrating the corrosive attack in a narrow straight line.

The second problem occurred some time later in a large outboard sternshaft seal fitted on an American merchant ship. When refitting, the superintendent of the line took our service engineer to task for supplying a shoddy product. He pointed out the large stainless steel bolts securing the seal to the hull. Their heads were drilled for wiring in pairs and he indicated several holes which appeared to have been drilled in the wrong place and left unused. The bolts were duly returned for inspection. This revealed a small barnacle snugly sitting at the bottom of each hole some of which were an inch deep. They too were producing a acidic glue resulting in the localised attack on the stainless.

To return to **SAUMAREZ'** propeller: the same story, careful examination of a green wart revealed a round jelly like growth which was getting enough moisture from condensation to survive and continue to produce a corrosive substance underneath it and the resulting pits are far too deep for polishing out.

Some may think that polishing propellers is going too far but a smooth surface on the blades certainly helps efficiency and is well worth preserving. A quick rub with a fine abrasive paper and a wipe with oil or grease when taking the boat out of the water must be well worth the effort.

38. PUMPS

Purpose:

Either to produce a flow of fluid, or to increase the pressure of a fluid. Term usually applied only to liquid handling machines - those for gases are usually referred to as fans or compressors.

Principle:

There are two main types: hydrodynamic and displacement. Hydrodynamic includes centrifugal and axial flow pumps. Displacement includes piston, gear, diaphragm and peristaltic pumps. We will concern ourselves solely with the piston/diaphragm types of displacement pumps, which are the most common in small boats.

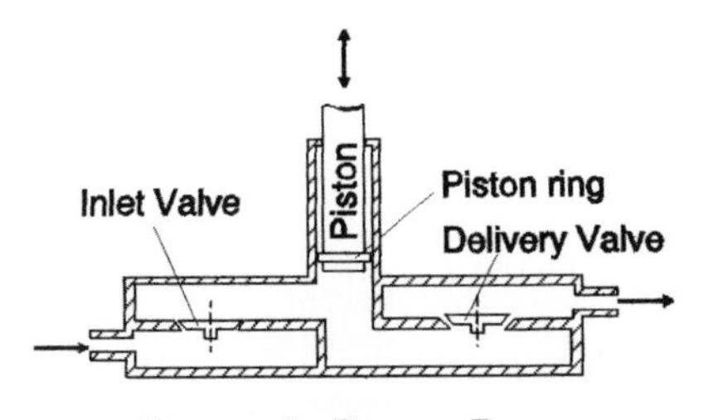

Figure 1: Piston Pump

Figure 1 shows a typical piston pump. When the piston is raised, water (or oil or other liquid) is drawn into the cylinder through the inlet valve. The delivery valve is held shut by the back pressure at outlet. When the piston is pushed down, the liquid is forced out through the delivery valve, and the inlet valve is closed.

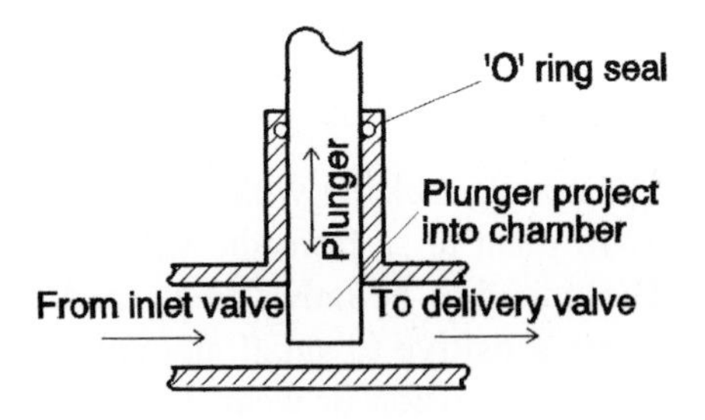

Figure 2: Plunger Pump

Figures 2 and 3 show some variants working on the same principle. The plunger pump is easier to make, while the diaphragm pump has less potential problem with leakage making it more suitable for liquid fuels or condenser extraction (the so called air pump).

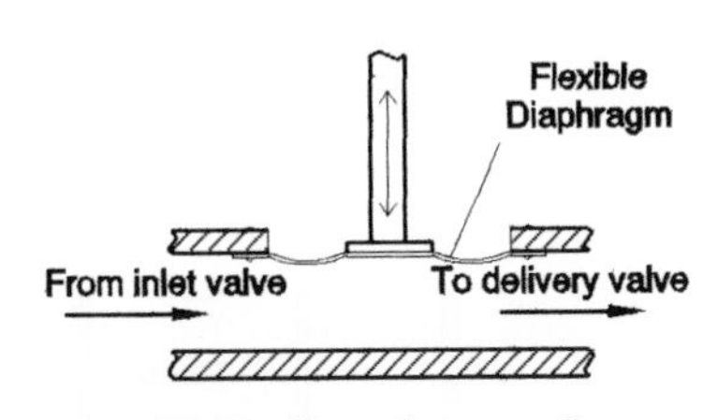

Figure 3: Diaphragm Pump

Displacement pumps produce the same amount of flow (approximately) for each stroke. This makes them suitable for engine driven feed pumps, since the steam consumption per stroke is also roughly constant.

Operation:

The main problems with pumps on small plant arise from the valves. These tend to be rather small, and so are sensitive to small amounts of dirt, corrosion or wear. If either valve leaks when it is supposed to be shut, the pump will work poorly if at all.

For best performance, the valves should be normally closed, and need a small pressure to open them. They can be kept closed by gravity or a spring. Figure 4 shows three common types of pump valves. The traditional type (a) is very satisfactory, but must be well maintained to keep a good seal. The ball bearing type (b) is easy to make. Note that the ball sits on a knife edge, not in a countersink. The ball should be stainless steel or bronze (or perhaps hard rubber or plastic); bearing balls are made of high carbon steel, and corrode rapidly. This type is re-seated by hitting it with a hammer, which distorts the knife edge to provide a snug fit. The flap valve (c) does not seem to be as widely used as it might be. At steamboat pressures and speeds, and low temperatures, there are many suitable rubber, plastic or composite materials which should be satisfactory.

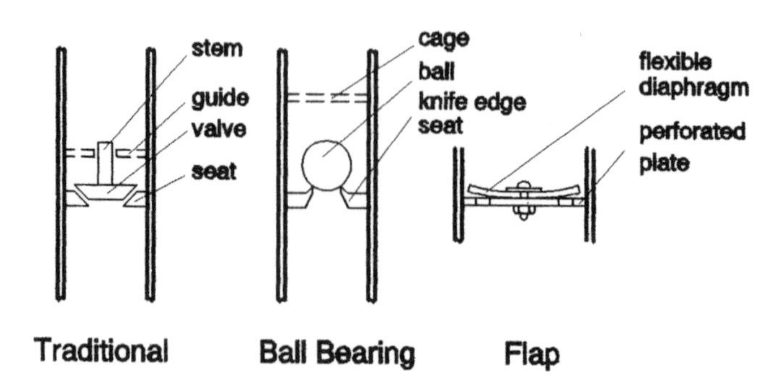

Figure 4: Valve Types

39. **REAMERS**

Reamers are like good wine - some mature to become old and trusted friends, others never reach perfection. Like taps, they often cut oversize when new and require careful 'running in'. Always use them with a very light oil - '3 in 1' is ideal. You can drive them with a power tool or lathe, but you will lose accuracy if the job heats up.

If you want to cut an accurate clearance hole, this can be achieved in the following way:

Cut a strip of approximately 200 grit wet-and-dry carborundum paper half the circumference of the hole. After reaming in the normal way, thread the strip into the full length of the hole with a similar length protruding, abrasive side to the metal. Ream the hole again, taking the paper through, trapping it. The reamer will cut through the paper, but repeating with new paper several times will progressively produce the required clearance.

40. **SAFETY I**

When the SBA introduced legislation to regulate the integrity of boilers in boats attending its events, a certain amount of dissent and discussion was naturally aroused. However, despite a degree of extra expense and inconvenience being inflicted on boat owners, the fundamental wisdom of the requirements has now been accepted and indeed has been overwhelmingly endorsed by more than one AGM.

It seems timely therefore to review some of the wider aspects of steamboating to see if there are any areas in which we should endeavour to move towards the same standards which we have set ourselves in boiler quality. In general terms the SBA Committee feel that it is the responsibility of the individual member to ensure that the boat is not a source of danger either to himself or, more importantly, to others, either in its construction or in the way in which it is used. It is this same sense of responsibility which is expected of boat owners when signing acceptance of the existing requirements and the waiver at the foot of every event booking form.

We would be more than happy to receive the ideas of members for improving safety; one specific topic which has been brought to our attention is the standard of installations in which propane gas is used as a fuel for steam boilers, and separate articles on this subject are included. Some other areas where comments and criticisms have arisen in recent years, and unfortunately on more than one occasion resulted in injury, are the integrity of pressurised structures outside the boiler, the carriage of fire fighting equipment and the precautions to be taken when venturing into coastal waters in small steam craft.

It is a statement of the obvious, but one which does not always seem to be fully appreciated, that anything attached to a steam boiler and capable of being pressurised by steam to the same level as the boiler itself should have the same standards of design and material integrity applied to it. This includes boiler fittings, particularly the gauge glass which should be large, sturdy, able to be isolated and periodically blown through and tested (the 'model' variety, as well as being weaker, are much more prone to blockage). Low lying drain and blow-down cocks should be protected from being trodden on if in vulnerable positions (it is a good idea for the blow-down cock to have a detachable handle). The pipework connecting boiler to engine is sometimes neglected; it should be of steam quality material, properly jointed and if necessary supported. As it is usually buried in lagging it should be periodically exposed and examined for corrosion and, as Sam Wilkinson has reminded us elsewhere, the vibration of the engine produces metal fatigue which should be counteracted by re-annealing at regular intervals.

A fact that is often overlooked is that the steam chests and cylinders of an engine are themselves pressure vessels, and a large cover held down by a few rusting studs is a potential lethal projectile. So due regard should be given to the pressure sustaining areas of covers vis-à-vis the number, quality and thickness of retaining studs when deciding on the pressure at which a particular engine should be run. (BS 10 on flange design gives useful guidance in this respect.)

Another statement of the obvious is that the average steamboat passenger is sitting within a virtually endless supply of fire extinguishing agent, and yet boats are frequently seen out without a bucket or other suitable container for making use of it. But water is by no means an ideal universal fire fighting medium. A fire in an inaccessible place such as beneath a boiler or floorboards is much more effectively dealt with by a suffocating agent such as BCF which has the added advantage of not flashing into scalding steam. All steamboats should carry at least one extinguisher - it can always be kept in the kitchen between outings and it save skulking from eagle-eyed lock keepers when out boating!

Finally, out to sea. Having experienced the discomfort of being caught in a worsening sea in failing light in a small ill-equipped glass-fibre boat, I can assure you there are few circumstances more likely to turn one instantly to religion. Please do not venture out into coastal waters unless you have a genuinely sea-worthy boat, a lifejacket for each person on board, a means of emergency propulsion, a good anchor and rope, a bailer and pump, a means of signalling distress and the confidence that you have checked the weather forecast.

41. SAFETY II

In recent years wee have heard a great deal about boiler insurance and boiler certificates as a requirement for all steamboats attending SBA meetings. A natural development of this is the need for more careful consideration of the risks relating to boiler design and, going on from that, the risks relating to all equipment in a steam boat, particularly as far as personal injury is concerned.

Ideally risks should be quantified since it must be acknowledged that there are levels of risk which are acceptable. For example, the very concept of being on the water in a boat implies a degree of risk which is freely accepted. In industry there has been a great deal of discussion about the degree of risk which is acceptable in a workshop or, for that matter, in offices, and the conclusion reached is that the only criterion is that of reasonableness. What is reasonable must inevitably be related to what is practical, what can be justified from the cost point of view, and also perhaps what has been given careful consideration.

This article has therefore been prepared to try to give a lead to a reasonable way of recognising the risks prevalent in a boat and to help to make judgements as to whether they are sufficiently serious to do something about. At the same time an attempt has been made to indicate what can be done to minimise risk. The action required is often so simple that, once the need is been made apparent, there can be no question that action is worth taking.

Boilers

In the writer's view the simple requirement to have a boiler certificate is not really adequate as a safety precaution applied arbitrarily to all boiler designs. To illustrate this, two simple questions should be answered about the plant concerned:

1. What volume of superheated water would be released if failure occurred?
2. Would the released steam be held in a secondary chamber in such a way that the majority would be conveyed up the funnel?

Most drum and fire-tube boilers contain a large amount of water, and they are rarely enclosed within a secondary leak-proof casing of sufficient strength to hold the released superheated water. By comparison, the capacity of most water-tube boilers is very much less and a casing is provided which would limit the effects of an escape due to tube failure.

In quantifying the two basic types, it would be reasonable to claim that serious personal injury to anyone in the vicinity of the boiler must be at least ten times more likely for the fire-tube and drum installations. The most common form of failure with a water tube boiler is tube failure and the rate of release will be controlled by the tube size. Thus the effects of such a failure will be more in the form of a controlled release of the contents of the boiler than an explosion.

The size of the tube relative to the boiler casing and funnel will also mean that the release of steam can be contained to a reasonable extent, and anyone in the vicinity would not be subjected to a direct jet of steam or superheated water.

With drum and fire-tube boilers, the most critical area is usually just at the water level where there is a tendency for the shell to corrode in a continuous line. The other most common form of failure is the water skirt or jacket surrounding the fire box. Other typically weak areas are those associated with a junction in rivetted plates or any arrangement which produces a crevice. Failure in places such as these, however, rarely results in a sudden and complete loss of boiler contents. The most common result is the appearance of a slight leakage which over a period of time develops to an unacceptable level but is not particularly dangerous. The real danger comes from a continuous line of corrosion at water level which weakens the drum in such a way that, when failure does occur, a massive rupture results. This allows the entire contents of the boiler to discharge which, in its worst form, is an explosion. Even at its best, there is an extremely dangerous situation of a large quantity of superheated water being projected in a particular direction before it has a chance to disperse. Frequent examination of drum and fire-tube boilers is the only real protection. In boilers of welded construction there may well be an argument for a reinforcing band round the drum at normal water level. The better the lagging casing is fitted to the boiler, the less the risk; however no lagging of a strength less than the boiler casing itself could possibly contain the energy released as a result of a massive rupture.

Pressure Tests

Pressure testing is a questionable assessment of the condition of a boiler, particularly of those incorporating relatively large drums. There is an argument that a hydraulic test of 50% above working pressure in such equipment can in fact stress the drum in such a way as to result in subsequent failure, even though the test itself shows nothing amiss. For water-tube boilers with small heavy wall drums, it is suggested that a pressure test of at least twice the working pressure is probably the best way of assessing the condition of the tubes because, in such designs, there is very little risk of a high stress situation leading to subsequent failure. Examination through the fire box of the tubes in any water-tube boiler, possibly by removing the casing, is one of the greatest safeguards. Tube failure is usually preceded by a long period of overheating. This can readily be recognised by the red appearance in such positions, as opposed to the light sooting that will normally be seen within the tube mass. Thus it could be said that the risk is reduced to 10% when drum boilers are opened up for inspection at frequent intervals - say two years, and tube boilers are hydraulically tested once a year and visually examined at least twice a year for tube burning.

Pipework

In most installations the material used for pipes is either copper or steel. Consideration has been given to using stainless steel, but there is a high risk with stainless that does not occur with the other two materials; when subjected to superheated steam for long periods, there is a tendency for stainless steel to develop a crystalline structure which makes it very susceptible to fracture, even though it appears to be in pristine condition. Steel tube is the best and safest proposition. However, it is liable to external corrosion - particularly under lagging - so it should be examined at frequent intervals.

The safest fittings to use with steel tube are those based on the compression of a ferrule on the tube incorporating a lip which actually bites into the surface. These are supplied by several companies, one of which is Ermeto. Brazed fittings may be used with steel, but there is a serious risk of destroying the strength of the steel during brazing in a way that cannot be seen until failure occurs in a relatively short time.

Copper tube, more commonly used, offers the safest solution to moderate temperature applications outside the boiler. It does, however, present some safety hazards if not treated correctly. In the first place, the gauge of copper tube used should be such that it is possible to bend it without risk of kinking in sizes up to ½" OD. Care should be taken to anneal the tubes before bending, and also preferably after bending and before installation. It is also a good idea to remove all the copper tubes from the installation about every other year for further annealing, for it does tend to harden, particularly if subjected to vibration. otherwise it may become so short in nature that it will eventually break. The best fittings to use with copper are the traditional bronze nipples and unions, silver soldered to the tube. It is possible to use compression fittings employing brass or copper ferrules, but they do present a safety hazard if certain precautions are not taken. The ideal way to use them is to compress them slightly on the tube, undo the fitting and run a trace of silver solder around the nut side of the ferrule where it is compressed onto the tube. This will not only prevent the necking of the tube that often occurs with these fittings, it will also prevent the tube working out of the fitting as a consequence of frequent temperature changes.

Fittings

Having decided the type of pipe to be used in various sections of the equipment, choose steel fittings with steel pipe and bronze fittings with copper pipe. Brass should only be used where low pressure cold water is being handled.

Gauge Glasses

The gauge glass is probably one of the most dangerous devices on the boiler because of unseen deterioration and risk of damage. It is essential to provide substantial protection round the glass, preferably both a solid metal sleeve and a toughened glass box. On smaller boilers it is often difficult to support the gauge glass fittings adequately, and a secondary stay running from the top fitting to the bottom may well be justified to stop the deflection of a fitting resulting in a broken glass. It is surprising how few people realise that the gauge glass is deteriorating the whole time that it is in operation. It is not uncommon to find quite serious erosion of the glass ends. The plug on the top fitting should be removed at least once a year to check the condition of the exposed end of the glass. It should be changed every two years anyway, as there is a tendency for the glass to become more brittle with the passage of time.

In a boat which carries a number of passengers, there is a lot to be said for considering the position of the gauge glass relative to them and, if they are directly exposed to the possibility of leakage from it and it cannot be put in a better position, a simple metal sheath can often be fitted without detriment to the operator's vision.

Whistles

The ideal position for a whistle in terms of safety may often be the worst position for it in terms of its effective operation. To work efficiently it must be kept warm and this normally dictates that it will be fitted immediately on top of the boiler. This has two disadvantages: (1) that it is in close proximity to the passengers, and (2) when it blows there is a tendency for it to prime, emitting a very dangerous jet of water as well as steam. here again, making sure that the opening faces away from the passengers and providing a simple sheath makes all the difference between a high risk and an acceptable one.

Fuel

The use of liquid or gas fuels on steam boats presents great advantage in terms of convenience but, at the same time, greatly adds to risk. The most common liquid fuel is paraffin or vapourising oil, and this has the great advantage that in cool liquid form it is almost impossible to ignite; the danger comes when it is heated or provided with a wick. For this reason care should be taken to prevent any fuel leaking from the burner from getting down into the bilges. Precautions that can be taken are to surround the firebox with mineral wool insulation which will act as a wick to burn off any leakage immediately it occurs when the boiler is in operation. Alternatively it will retain the liquid so that it will burn off when the boiler is next in operation. The next defence should be a liquid-tight sump tank large enough to contain a high proportion of the total fuel carried, and also to prevent slopping into the bilges due to the vessel's motion at sea.

Waste material should never be left in the bilges or the sump as this is the one thing that would make ignition possible.

Gas presents similar problems in that it is heavier than air and will normally drain either into a sump tank or the bilge, but it has the further disadvantage that it cannot be seen and that it will ignite instantly once a certain concentration of gas and air is reached. The first and most obvious precaution is to provide a sump tank, closely followed by frequent checks on any pipe fittings in the gas system. These can readily be carried out with a small brush and soapy water. Such precautions however do not eliminate the problems of the system being not properly shut down. In an open boat the risks are relatively small in that the wind will tend to clear the hull of gas. But if the bilges are covered by a sole or flooring, there is always a risk of explosion resulting from gas lying in the sheltered space provided. The one real protection that can be taken is to provide some form of gas detection which requires electricity. In general terms, good practice would be to ensure that only one person is on board when first lighting up.

Many river authorities lay down that storage tanks for gas or oil should be surrounded by a secondary liquid-tight compartment with an overboard drain. This is such a simple precaution that there can be no excuse for not installing this vital piece of equipment in the correct manner.

42. **SAFETY III**

At the AGM a member spoke of the need for the SBA to consider safety rules for members.

Many aspects of safety in boats fall under the heading of "Good Seamanship" and I leave discussion of those to better qualified members than myself, but I offer in this article some guidelines based on the regulations for "the Carriage of Passengers in Ships and Motor Vessels including those Plying on Inland rivers, Canals, Estuaries and Lakes" and the "Merchant Shipping Safety Rules (Fire Appliances)" and "(Life Saving Appliances)".

Many people may not, I think, be aware that the Department of Transport provides regulations under the merchant Shipping Acts, some of which are applicable in law to any size or type of pleasure boat and some which, though mandatory only for pleasure boats of 45 ft or over, nevertheless provide useful guidelines for owners of smaller craft.

Passengers (information from MS notice M913)

No ship (this means virtually anything that floats) may proceed to sea or on any voyage or excursion with more than twelve passengers on board unless it holds a valid Passenger Certificate issued by the Department of Transport.

"Passenger" means any person carried whether or not for a fare except:

(a) a person engaged in any capacity on board the ship on the business of the ship,
(b) children under one year of age.

Owners and masters have been prosecuted and convicted for carrying more than twelve passengers without a certificate.

Fire Appliances, Class XII
(Pleasure yachts 45 ft and over)

Any open ship of less than 70 ft shall be provided with two fire extinguishers or two fire buckets, one of which shall be provided with a lanyard. In addition, any ship of Class XII which is fitted with oil-fired boilers shall be provided with two portable fire extinguishers suitable for extinguishing oil fires.

Life Saving Appliances, Class XII

Every ship of less than 70 ft which operates in smooth waters, i.e. lakes, rivers, canals and estuaries within defined limits shall carry at least two lifebuoys and a buoyant line of at least 60 ft in length. In addition, for every person on board, a lifejacket must be carried (semi-inflatable jackets are allowed). Children's jackets must be carried for those weighing less than 70 lbs.

Stowage and Handling

Lifebuoys shall be stowed so as to be readily accessible to all persons on board and in such a position that they can be readily cast loose

Lifejackets shall be stowed so as to be readily accessible to all persons on board. Their position shall be clearly and permanently indicated.

Finally, a word about the usefulness of lifebuoys. As well as being a possible means of support for a person in the water, it also acts as a conspicuous marker for the helmsman of the rescuing boat. It is therefore important that a lifebuoy has sufficient self-weight to prevent its being rapidly blown away by the wind. There are some very light expanded foam lifebuoys on the market and I know from personal experience that they are not reliable as markers. It is a good idea to have an additional lifebuoy secured to the buoyant line. This can then be used when the rescue boat approaches the victim to enable him or her to be pulled alongside or to the bank.

43. **SAFETY AT SEA**

Hazards

Sand and mud banks in estuaries can be a hazard, leaving you high and dry until the next high tide. It helps to know your channel marks; banks are edged by yellow posts, withies or buoys with top marks in the form of cones. The north edge of a bank is marked by two cones pointing upwards, the south edge by two cones pointing downwards. East - two cones, one above the other, base to base. West - two cones, one above the other, apex to apex.

Man Overboard!

On a fine summer's day, do a 'Man Overboard' exercise. You may be very surprised to discover how difficult it is to haul someone semi-conscious back into your boat. The first stage is to secure a rope round the body under the arms, secured with a bowline, *NOT* a slip-knot. Pass the rope round some secure object in the middle of the boat. Then experiment with one or two people trying to get the inert body back on board without the victim's help. You will probably find that coming in over the stern is the only way in a small boat. Over the side may be the best proposition in a larger boat, in which case a stiff mast to give a high lead point for the rope will be a great help.

Fire at Sea!

I have experienced it in **SAUMAREZ** in rough weather; certainly frightening when you discover, too late, that most fire extinguishers *do not work very well* in a high wind. The dry powder type is absolutely useless. By good fortune, I had a soot-blowing steam lance rigged at my moment of truth. It put a sizeable sump fire and the main oil burner out in seconds. Ever since, I have always had the steam lance rigged and readily accessible and I cannot commend too strongly this safety measure; steam quality hose is essential for the lance. Obviously, if you have gas cooking on board as we do, you must have a secondary extinguisher as well.

44. THE SAFETY VALVE

Purpose:

The purpose of a safety valve is to prevent the steam pressure in the boiler rising above a safe value, dependent on the boiler design and condition, by releasing steam to the atmosphere. It should never operate in normal conditions.

The term (and the device) is sometimes confused with *relief valve*, whose pressure is to control the pressure at a desired level. Many small boiler users expect the same device to fill both roles, which is often quite satisfactory.

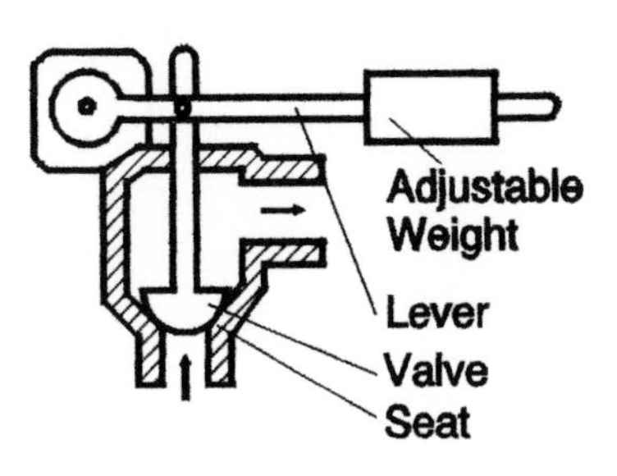

Figure 1
Dead-weight Safety Valve

Principle:

The steam is applied to a valve face which is held against its seat either by a weight (figure 1) or a spring (figure 2). When the pressure rises to the set value, the valve opens either abruptly (most common with safety valves) or progressively (more usual with relief valves).

The valve is usually so constructed that it cannot be held closed from outside (either accidentally or deliberately). The set pressure adjustment is often lockable to prevent tampering.

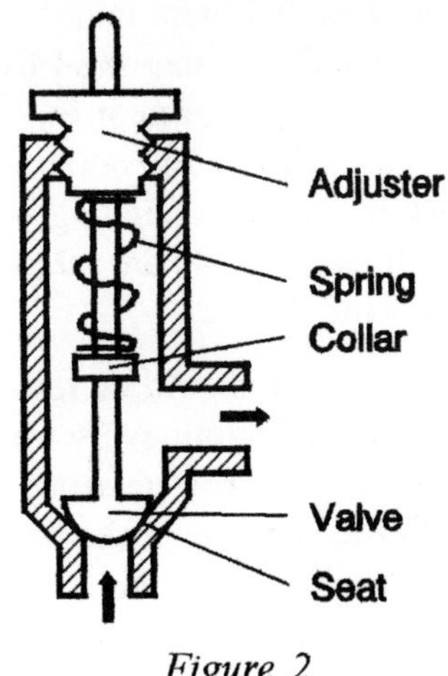

Figure 2
Spring Safety Valve

Operation:

A safety valve must be fitted directly to the boiler top drum and to any other heated part of the system which can be isolated (such as a superheater). The valve must be capable of accepting the full evaporation rate of the boiler, and its outlet pipe must open directly to atmosphere.

The valve must be set to the correct pressure. While the general range is fixed by the spring or weight used, the final adjustment must be done by trial and error, using a good quality pressure gauge. The Boiler Inspector will check that the set pressure is not too high and that there is no *accumulation* - i.e. that the valve, when operating, is getting rid of the steam as fast as the boiler can produce it. Typical operating points for small steam boats are 60 psi to 150 psi (4 to 10 bar).

In use the valve should be tested frequently (preferably every time steam is raised). Any tendency to stick (fail to open) or leak (fail to close properly) should be investigated as soon as possible.

45. **SEAMANSHIP I**

On several occasions it has been suggested that a few words on seamanship would be welcomed by boat owners in the SBA. it is possible that many steamboat owners are so absorbed with engines and boilers that seamanship tends to go by the board. Although I very much doubt if I am the best informed member for the task, here are some thoughts on the subject. I have tried to illustrate the basic essentials as they might occur on a steamboat outing.

Launching

(a) Have a good look at the ramp and establish where it finishes under water. Plan your intentions.

(b) Explain your plan to your crew and make sure they know what is expected of them.

(c) Make sure that the hubs on your trailer are cold. If not, pour cold water on them until they are cold; if not, they will suck water into the bearings when you submerge them.

(c) Plan where you are going to moor when launched, which will indicate whether or not someone will have to be aboard when slipping. If there are no moorings, consider getting steam up while the boat is on the trailer, or even just lighting the fire.

Mooring Alongside

For this exercise we will assume that there is a proper pontoon with bollards and that the boat is going

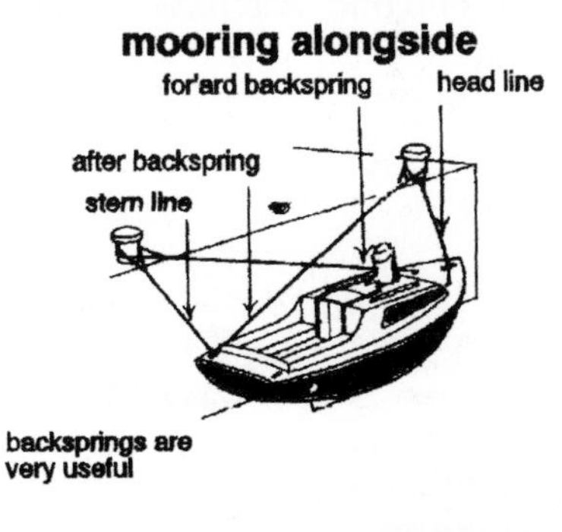

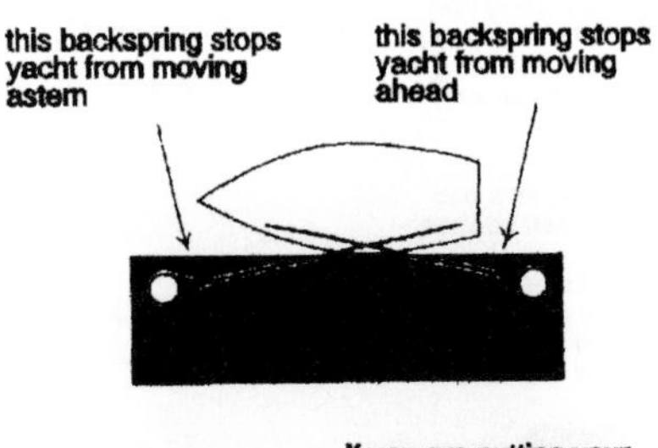

If you are putting your rope on a post which already has a mooring on it, pass yours up through the other so it can be let go before yours.

You can put a temporary eye in a rope with a bowline.

to be left overnight on a tidal stream.

(a) Come alongside heading into the stream.
(b) Secure the bow line first. The bollard should be well forward of the stem of the boat. There should be a spliced eye at the end of the rope to place over the bollard; if not, a temporary eye may be formed with a bowline. Alternatively take the end of the line back to the boat which will also make casting-off simpler; this also applies when mooring to rings.
(c) If you are putting your rope on a post that already has a mooring on it, pass yours up through the loop of the other so that it can be let go before yours.
(d) Adjust the line on the fitting on your boat. Never use knots on fittings on shore which make it difficult for other people to use them. If they do you will have your work cut out to untangle your line when you sail.
(c) Next, secure the stern line well aft of the boat, bearing the above in mind.
(f) Fix two backsprings, one from an aft position on the boat to the forward bollard or post, the other from a forward position on the boat to the aft bollard ((b) and (c) apply again). if you had used knots on the bollards they would already look like a cat's breakfast with only your boat tied up.

knots

reef knot

For joining two ropes of similar size and tying 'reef points'

sheet bend

For joining two ropes of different sizes and tying a rope to an eye splice

round turn and two half hitches

The most common way of making a rope's end fast to a post or bollard

bowline

A loop that will not slip. Uses include **securing a lifeline** round a person's waist and making an eye in the end of a mooring line to throw over a bollard

Casting Off

(a) Ascertain the direction of the current and the wind.
(b) Remove backsprings after warming engine.
(c) Make sure you have a full head of steam.
(d) Let go the downstream line first, then the last one with the engine turning slowly. If you have to move off astern, centre the helm before turning the engine and remember that the boat will swing due to propeller rotation before you get steering way. This can be countered with short bursts ahead with half rudder during the astern manoeuvre.
(e) If there is a very strong off-shore wind try to let both lines go at the same time. If on-shore, get a good angle to the bank before casting off.

Passengers and Crew

If you wish to display good seamanship it is essential that everyone in your boat knows what is expected of them. This means that you must have a few words with them before you get ready to cast off.

(a) Ask if everyone in the boat can swim in their clothes. You will then have some idea who to help first in an emergency.
(b) Tell them where the lifebelts and fire extinguishers are stowed and how to use them.
(c) Tell them if you want them all to grab the jetty when coming alongside, or to wait for your instructions before doing anything. Few people seem to realise that if they stop the boat's movement before you are ready you lose steering way and control resulting in a messy operation of which you will not be proud.
(d) Tell them where to sit in order to trim the boat to your satisfaction.
(e) Tell them where to climb back into your boat if they fall in or have a swim.
(f) Tell them that you will give clear instructions during the cruise and **do so**:
E.g.
"Cast off Aft"
"Cast off Forward"
"Take in Fenders"

Under Way

(a) Make sure that the helm is manned at all times.
(b) Keep a sharp look-out.
(c) Keep to the right of the channel unless clearly instructed otherwise.
(d) You have right of way over small powered and rowing craft on your **port** side.
(e) You must give way to all vessels approaching from your **starboard** side, all vessels under sail, and large boats and ships constrained by the channel. If in doubt, give way to the latter in all circumstances.
(f) Regardless of your rights, the ultimate responsibility for avoiding a collision rests with the master of the boat.

Channel Marks

(a) Looking forward, the left side is *port* and *red*, the right side is *starboard* and *green*. To help remember this there is a little aid which runs:

Red stop, left in port,
Green go right ahead.

(b) Running against the normal current (e.g. up an estuary or river, or up the Channel into the North Sea), marks or buoys on the left are **red** and on the right are **green**.
(c) Banks are marked with yellow buoys. The normal practice is to place them at the North, South, East and West extremities where there will be water at low-water springs. To be of any use they must indicate which edge they are marking, and this is shown by a system of black cones mounted on top of them as follows:

North:2 cones pointing upwards;
South: 2 cones pointing downwards;
East: 2 cones pointing away from each other;
West: 2 cones pointing towards each other.

The aid to help you remember this runs as follows:

Western women are wasp-waisted;
Eastern women are pregnant.

(d) To be on the safe side in an estuary a chart is essential.

(e) You can signal your intentions with your whistle, as follows:
One blast: I am altering course to starboard;
Two blasts: I am altering course to port;
Three blasts: my engines are going astern.

It is far more important to keep a good look-out.

Flags

Flags should only be flown when the sun is above the horizon. Strictly speaking the ensign should be flown when the vessel is in commission or when the master is on board.

46. SEAMANSHIP II

Everybody who read *New Members Start Here* should by now have a boat and be eagerly awaiting instructions as to what to do with her.

The answer is simple - enjoy yourself! But to do that properly you have to know what you are doing. That falls into two parts: managing the boat and managing the steam plant.

Managing the Boat

Managing a steamboat is similar to managing any other sort of boat, and comes down to a combination of following rules and following commonsense (or experience, which is and should be much the same thing). The rules are many and varied, but usually only a few are relevant.

Rules of Navigation:

The most basic rule of all is that the Master of any ship is completely and solely responsible for her safety. Advice and information may be given by other people, charts, navigation marks and so on, but the final decision is with the Master.

The fundamental rules are The International Rules for the Prevention of Collisions at Sea. The word "collisions" is vital; if there is no risk of collision, the rules do not apply. These rules may be supplemented, or very occasionally varied, by rules laid down by navigation authorities in particular places.

Steamboats, like motor boats, take a rather low priority in the rules. They must in all cases give way to sailing or man-powered boats (though a sailing boat which is under power, even though it may be under sail as well, counts as a motor boat). If you are not familiar with sailing, always give sailing boats a wide berth and try to pass astern of them. If you are an experienced sailor, it is reasonable to make an intelligent guess as to what the boat is likely to do next. (Incidentally, sailing boats engaged in a race do not thereby acquire extra priority, even over other sailing boats.)

Steamboats must also give way to larger vessels whose freedom to manoeuvre is limited, either by restricted waterways (e.g. channel ferries in Portsmouth harbour) or by inability to change course quickly (channel ferries outside Portsmouth harbour), or by their activity (fishing or towing). Much the best way of giving this priority is never to go near them in the first place. If none of these applies, then you give priority to any vessel approaching from your starboard side (right hand, facing forward) or to any boat you are overtaking. If you are approaching another boat *head on*, then each must alter course to pass to starboard (keep right).

About the only time you have priority is over a similar sized power boat approaching from your port side. If you have priority, you *must* take it. This means maintaining your course and speed, or carrying out a completely predictable manoeuvre such as going alongside a jetty.

Unfortunately, there are water users (usually speedboats) who do not understand or abide by these rules. Give them a wide berth.

In this connection, there is another and vital rule of the road which says, in effect, that in the final analysis, even if it is your right of way, if it looks at the last moment that if nothing is done there is going to be a collision, then each vessel shall take such action as shall best serve to avoid collision.

Signals:

There are many internationally agreed signalling systems, but the one most relevant here is the use of the whistle. Purists say that the whistle should only be used for signals, but this is extreme. After all, high spirits, showing off and frightening horses can all be thought of as communication. The important thing is not so much that your signals should be understood by everyone, but that they should not be misunderstood by anyone. So make it clear that your informal whistle is not a signal, or else make it a signal for what you were going to do anyway.

The most common standard signals are:

1 blast: altering course to starboard;
2 blasts: altering course to port;
3 blasts: engine (not necessarily boat) going astern;
5 or more blasts: emergency.

These are commonly supplemented by local rules which may, for instance, distinguish between long and short blasts, or may as on the Thames and Tideway, have codes for going about.

The other signal used by most steamboats is the wearing of an ensign (n.b. flags only *fly* ashore). This means 'The master is aboard and in effective control'. Think carefully before raising the ensign after lunch at an SBA rally!

Common Sense:

Common sense is, by its very nature, difficult to summarise. The only way to acquire it is from experience - both your own and other people's and by continually asking "What if...?" Boats and their operation are inherently hazardous, but it is nearly as useless to say "Never try anything new" as to say "Try anything once". The way to learn is to take small risks, where the consequences may be scratching paint or getting wet, but not large ones which could terminate the career of boat and/or crew.

Never take your boat out if you are doubtful about the conditions (this applies in coastal waters, lakes or fast flowing rivers, rarely in canals). Never venture far from the shore (or a nearby escort boat) if you are doubtful about the reliability of your plant. Always seek local advice about wind, tide, current, channels, shelter, depths, etc. Always believe warnings but be sceptical about reassurances.

Always carry a spare of almost anything. Have a long length of rope on board in addition to your normal mooring ropes and anchor warp. Carry at least two paddles or oars; carry something that can be used as a bailer, even if you have a bilge pump. Carry extra protective clothing, or at least a tarpaulin or boat cover which can be used for extra protection and warmth. Carry another box of matches in a screw top jar in a locker, with the emergency supply of canned beer.

Managing the Steam Plant

Two considerations: firstly, make sure it's safe; secondly, keep it working. Safety has only two aspects: the safety valve must be in good working order and adequate, and the water level in the boiler must be maintained (the preferred level is between half and two-thirds up the glass, but anywhere visible is safe). Given these two, the boiler will not explode, although plenty of less spectacular forms of damage are possible.

Looking after the engine is reasonably easy. All that it needs is a head of steam, occasional oil, and the drains opening if it is cold. The working controls are the throttle (or regulator) and the reversing link, whose operation is fairly obvious.

The boiler is another matter; you must maintain an adequate pressure under the varying conditions you will encounter. This can take a considerable degree of skill, particularly with solid fuel. The controls available are the water feed, the fuel and the air. Feeding water into the boiler tends to reduce the steam pressure; putting fuel on the fire initially cools the fire down, lowering the pressure, then probably raises it as the fire builds up again. Cutting down the air will normally reduce the pressure, though if you had too much air to start with, it might raise it.

All these controls interact, and you cannot rely on any one of them alone. There comes a time when you must put the feed on; if you're short of pressure at the time, you may be in trouble. If you open the damper and turn on the blower, you will be fine for a while, but then the fire will go out for lack of fuel. You must always be juggling them; 'little and often' is the rule for all of them, and always keep a bit in reserve all round. Remember too that though the safety valve will stop the pressure from rising too much, it does so by allowing steam to escape, thus wasting water. This can be quite a nuisance when waiting with the engine stopped (e.g. in a lock).

The load on the boiler also affects the steam pressure. The load comes from two sources: steam used by the engine and auxiliaries and heat lost to the surroundings. The latter depends on the weather. If you are steaming downwind with the sun out things are usually easier than battling against a cold head wind. Usually, opening the throttle will increase the steam consumption, though if you are a puffer, the extra draught may maintain the pressure for you and the increased speed of an engine-driven feed pump will maintain the water level.

Maintaining your pressure with varying demand is quite a skill. A typical SBA rally involves raising steam early, finding your crew have disappeared, waiting for them, steaming to a passenger pick-up point, waiting for *them*, steaming for about two hours with several stops for swing bridges or locks, stopping for lunch, then the whole thing in reverse (with a tea stop). Keeping a fire lit and a useful steam pressure, without blowing off, needs practice and luck. One soon learns to put a lump of wet wood (or a disposable nappy) on a fire when a lock comes in sight, to use the injector or a hand pump in the lock, and to turn the blower on again just as the gates are opening.

Everyone runs out of steam from time to time. Everyone runs aground, breaks down and gets weed on the prop. Everyone thinks that everyone else manages better than they do. But everyone finds out that everyone else does not manage much better than them. Very few people get into serious trouble. Come along and have a go at actually doing it, rather than just reading FUNNEL.

47. **SILVER SOLDER**

Silver solder is the steamboat builder's best friend. It has endless uses from pipe joints, adapting pipe fittings, fabricating small pumps to fabricating special fittings for the hull. To carry out work of any size, two efficient gas blowlamps will be required, nozzle size about 1", and a collection of small fire bricks. BAXI supply domestic coal fire-back bricks which are ideal. Good quality flux is essential; last, but most important, the right silver solder. Cheaper substitutes are available but, to be honest, I do not trust them. Those that I have tried worked on simple applications such as joining bronze nipples to copper pipe, but on more complex jobs, if requiring heat for a long time they seem to degenerate into a frustrating uncooperative mess.

Therefore I would recommend only genuine silver solder made by Johnson Mathey, or similar. It should be available at about £2.00 for $\frac{1}{16}$" diameter rod, 18" long. Buy flux when you buy the rod.

Preparation is important - work pieces must be bright metal, free from grease or oil. Use dry-cleaning fluid; if the face will not wet with clean water, abrade it with fine paper or degrease it until it does. Flux the surface as follows:

(a) Wet the surface of the metal where the joint is to be made, then dip in flux which should adhere to the wetted surface only. Then heat, applying the flame very carefully so as not to blow the flux away as it dries. The risk of this quickly passes as the flux melts and adheres.

(b) Alternative method: put a small quantity of flux in a glass or plastic container, quarter fill with a tea cup with water and add 1 only drop of washing-up liquid. Add the treated water to the flux a drop at a time until it mixes into a thick paste. Only a fraction of the water will be required. Paint the paste onto the surface to be soldered; if it does not stick moisten it a whisker more.

Now set the joints up on one of the larger fire-bricks and support them securely with the smaller ones. If you have a wooden bench, put a steel plate on it under the brick. Alternatively, stand the brick on the open jaws of the vice. Check your set by tapping the brick with your torch; if secure, proceed.

Get the torch stabilised at full blast, heat the end of the rod slightly and dip it into the flux which, if hot enough will stick to it. Heat the work pieces, making sure the flux is not blown off. If it is, add a little more from the end of the rod; then reflux the rod end as above.

Keep the heat on the work and watch the flux. As red heat approaches the flux should become glass-like and completely cover the work surfaces. Now touch the work pieces with the fluxed rod out of the flame; after a moment or two it should melt and quickly spread over the prepared surfaces by capillary attraction.

Continue to add solder until small fillets appear in the corners. Take the rod away and continue to heat all round until there is no remaining meniscus at the edge of the solder. Turn off the torch. Plunge the workpiece in water. Wipe off any traces of flux while still wet.

Silver Soldering in a Vice

When doing a tricky silver-soldering job it can be a great help to hold the assembly together in a vice. The vice may act as a massive heat soak making it almost impossible to make a sound joint. This problem can be overcome by the use of mineral-wool lagging tape. Take a strip round the back of the workpiece and between it and the vice jaws on each side. This will concentrate the heat and eliminate the heatsoak.

48. SLIDE VALVE

Purpose:

The flat slide valve (sometimes called a "D" valve) admits boiler steam to the cylinder and releases exhaust steam at appropriate points in the cycle. Although there are many other types of valve, this is by far the most common in small steamboat installations.

Principle:

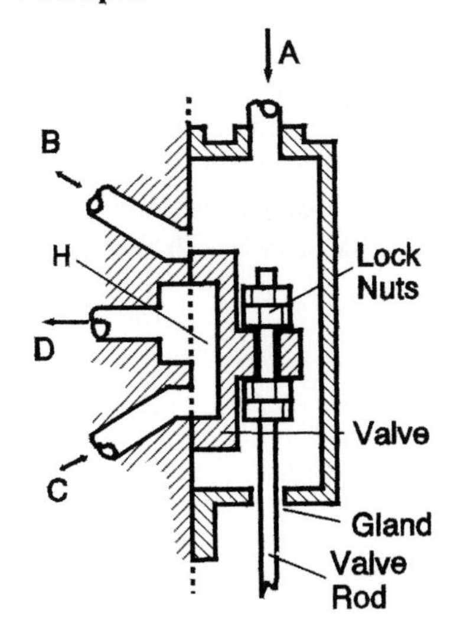

The illustration shows a typical flat valve system for a double acting cylinder. Boiler steam is supplied through *port A*. As the valve moves up and down, the steam is allowed alternately to the upper side of the piston (through *port B*) and the lower side (through *port C*). At the same time, the other port is connected to *port D* through the hollow of the valve (*H*). The exhaust steam then passes to the next cylinder, the condenser or the blast pipe, according to the type of engine.

Operation:

To avoid leakage, the valve must be in smooth sliding contact with the valve face. This is usually ensured by the steam pressure which, being higher outside than in, holds the valve to the face. (Occasionally, engines are reversed by swapping supply and exhaust ports. In this case the valve has to be held against the face by some mechanical means.) To avoid near-impossible problems of alignment, the valve must be able to 'float' a little on the rod so that it seats nicely.

Two metal surfaces in sliding contact must be lubricated to avoid high friction losses and undue wear. If wet steam is used a water film forms between the two and acts as a lubricant. It is, however, rather inefficient and cannot withstand high steam pressures. For high pressure running or where superheated steam is used, oil must be supplied, either through special passages in the block (difficult) or as a mist in the steam (much more common). For very high pressures, the load can be reduced by isolating the steam supply from the back of the valve or another type of valve, such as the piston valve, can be used.

The flat slide or "D" valve has several virtues which other types do not. It is quite happy and is self-adjusting against wear or wide manufacturing tolerances, and, by simply lifting off the face, it can relieve excess pressure caused, for example, by water condensing in the cylinder.

The design of the valve and valve gear determines the various parameters such as lead, lap, cut-off, travel etc. On double-acting reversing engines (most SBA engines), the valve system has to be more or less symmetrical. The only control provided is normally the reversing link which simultaneously changes several things. On the ubiquitous *Stephenson's Link* valve gear it is often worthwhile controlling the speed by "linking up" rather than "throttling back". This, by reducing the time the ports are uncovered, reduces the amount of steam used without reducing the pressure at admission. This increases the expansion ratio of the engine and reduces the steam consumption more or less in line with the power.

49. **SLIPWAYS**

It was at the social seminar at Bourton. A group of us were sitting round a table enjoying our last relaxed meal when the subject of launching came up.

"It was some time", said Bill Selby, "before I realised that I wasn't the only one worried about getting his boat out at the end of a rally - nearly everyone is". (That is, if they've already got it safely into the water in the first place, I thought.)

Bill went on to tell of the first few worrying occasions he launched and retrieved his boat **SERENA**. one memorable occasion being when all four trailer support bars stood on end and were in danger of puncturing the hull as a friend, though warned to drive slowly, raced up the slipway while Bill held his breath and, according to his wife, turned white.

The ensuing conversation brought forth a catalogue of disasters and near-disasters experienced by members in the simple act of getting their boats down into the water. Bill's crisis was not nearly as bad as poor Ron Thorougood's whose **SOOTY** actually was punctured and sunk when being launched.

Of course there are simpler ways of sinking on launching; Derrick left the bung out of **OXBIRD** on arrival in Denmark and James Robinson gave a yell as the water rushed in. Denny admits leaving the bung out no less than three times - once with **FIREFLY** and twice with **MARIAMNE**, though on each occasion managing to get the bung back in time to prevent the boat actually going down.

The pleasure of actually floating the boat off the trailer and successfully tying her up tends to make one forget about the trailer itself. Bill Lowe's trailer once disappeared off the end of the slip at Beaulieu and Adrian Birtles had to wade into the water to get a line on it; Bill had to wait till the tide turned before being able to retrieve it.

Talking of Beaulieu, a most unfortunate event occurred when Nick Knight having **NATALIE** swinging in the Bremmer boat-lift went off to the car park to collect the trailer, only to find it had been 'nicked'. There was a maddening postscript to this episode. A wife of one of the members, her suspicions aroused by the behaviour of someone furtively hitching up an empty trailer in the park, actually noted down the number of the car. Alas, when it was realised that the driver was indeed the villain concerned, the piece of paper with the number on it had been destroyed.

One way or another, Committee members seem particularly prone to disaster. There was an occasion when one of them walked off the end of the slipway right up to his neck at the first Orford rally; another Committee member ran an old Austin 7 right into the water behind his boat (my namesake; the boat, not the member). Then there was a certain Noble Lord who lit his Merryweather boiler before entering the water, and seeing a blank gauge glass, assumed that it was full. It wasn't....

'Lifeboat launches' are the speciality of Sam Wilkinson. At Oxford this year the wire snapped halfway down the slipway and **SAUMAREZ** shot off into the water; she would have ended up in Oxford if she hadn't been caught at the bridge.

SAUMAREZ had learnt to enjoy this prank at Exeter. Being too high to be lifted by the crane, she was towed by Sam round to the other side of the river where there was a slip of sorts. By "of sorts" I mean that the slip ended at the water's edge and didn't run on into the water. Sam's plan was to use the 'break-back' and let the boat down into the water on the wire. When the wire broke, **SAUMAREZ** dived stern-first into the Exe with a spectacular splash. Fortunately the stern doors of the cabin were both well-made and shut and she bobbed up like a cork, coming to no harm.

Rope burns, acquired when trying to avert disaster, are a hazard one does not think about - until it happens.

Derrick disowns me for writing this article; however he did mention the occasion when somebody launched a boat still tied to her trailer, both sailing off together.

Denny suggests that, strangely enough, no-one has yet achieved the most obvious calamity of launching: that of steering off the slipway sideways so that everything capsizes pulling the car in after it - perhaps I had better not go on......

All this leads one to think up a few

Rules when Slipping:

1. Check the time of the tide;

2. Always attach a rope to boat and trailer;

3. Always take two round turns about a tree or other fixed point;

4. Make sure the bung is in;

5. Make sure there are no sharp points on the trailer;

6. Make sure the brakes are on securely on the towing vehicle;

7. Always leave your trailer in as safe a place as possible and **LOCK IT**!

50. **SPANISH WINDLASS**

If you are building a boat, do not forget the shipwright's friend - the Spanish Windlass. If you are springing rubbing strakes into position on a hull and working on your own, they are a great blessing; simply one turn of rope right round the hull, tightened with a short length of timber forced through the loop and twisted round and round. A small cord should be tied to the rope before starting which is used to secure the timber in the tightened position.

51. **STAINLESS STEEL - BEWARE!**

Sad to say, a piece of good quality cast iron is safer in sea water than stainless steel, particularly the common grade 316. Stainless suffers from intercrystalline corrosion, which destroys the bond between the particles from which it is formed.

Unfortunately, there may not be any outward evidence of this but it results in a drastic loss of strength, which can be very dangerous in components under pressure or stress.

52. **STEERING CABLES**

Nice to have a steering position amidships, but often difficult to run a reliable control system to the stern of the boat.

One solution is to use good quality multi-strand stainless steel cable just below ¼" diameter in a ¼" nylon air pressure pipe. The two right angle turns in the corners of the transom should be accomplished with pulleys and bare wire. Then maintain not less than 6" radii in the nylon tube to the steering position, using the standard clips available. If you want to maintain a steamboat all metal concept, put the nylon inside suitable copper pipe. *Note*: it does not work very well if you try to dispense with the low friction lining. Use cycle chain and a rear wheel sprocket on the steering wheel. The cable can be spliced through the last link at each end of the chain or secured with splicing clips.

53. **STUD DRIVING**

This can be a tedious process particularly when dealing with a large number of small studs. The answer is to use a drill chuck and there are several ways of taking advantage of this simple solution. A hand-drill is ideal for small studs, a hand brace for medium sizes, and a Jacob's chuck which can be tightened with a key and turned with a clamp on its tail for the larger sizes. It will be found that even if you have to grip the thread no damage of any consequence will result.

54. **TIPS ON TAPS**

New Taps

A brand new tap will normally cut a few thou oversize. If you want a really tight thread fit, it is a good idea to do a test on another piece of similar material first. After cutting ten threads in steel, the tap will lose the excessive edge sharpness causing the trouble.

Broken Taps

Disaster! - the tap breaks just as the job is completed. There are a few ways of recovering the situation which have worked for me over the years.

(a) Find a split pin that will fit into the grooves in the broken tap in the hole. Bend it over backwards to form a 'U' shape. Only suitable for four groove taps which allow the 'U' shape to be inserted, leaving a loop for a bar over the top. Make sure that any loose bits of tap have been removed and the hole filled with a light oil or release agent before attempting to unscrew with an oscillating movement.

(b) Soften the tap with a fine oxy-acetylene flame, and drill out.

(c) Grind the short end of an Allen key (smaller than the tap) to match, roughly, the shape of the exposed broken end of the tap. After fluxing the end of the Allen key, apply a blob of silver solder. Reflux the blob and wipe off the surplus. Hold against the broken end of the tap and heat until a bond is achieved, lubricate and remove.

(d) For very small taps, drill from the reverse side and drive out with a hard punch. Re-tap right through and use a longer screw or thread.

(e) With great caution, burn out with nitric or sulphuric acid, after consulting a chemist.

(f) Take to a tool making company which has a tap-removing service (usually employing spark erosion).

(g) With a very hard small punch, patiently and progressively break up the tap in the hole. Often effective if only two or three threads have been cut. However, this should be the last resort because it makes other methods difficult if it fails.

55. THRUST BLOCK

Purpose:

To transfer the thrust generated by the propeller from the propeller shaft to the boat.

Principle:

The rotation of the propeller generates thrust which is passed up the shaft. At some point, this has to be transferred to the hull of the boat (where the resisting forces are). Few engines are designed to take endways forces on the crankshaft, so another bearing has to be provided.

Operation:

The thrust block may be positioned anywhere between the propeller and the engine. The most convenient place to put it is where the shaft enters the boat, on the inside. Here, it can be securely anchored to the keel, and can double up as the inboard bearing of the propeller shaft, locating it against side loads (principally its weight). It also leaves the maximum space inside the boat for things like universal joints and couplings, which also do not like end loads.

Big ship thrust blocks are complicated pieces of machinery, with many independent bearing faces all of which have to be set up to take their share of the load and need lubrication. Small boats are much more straightforward, since the propelling forces are usually of the order of a few tens of pounds. (To get an idea how big, imagine towing one boat with another - how tight is the tow rope?) A typical propeller shaft is around 1 inch diameter. Many commercially available ball bearing races of this diameter can easily take the required thrust. One of the most appropriate types is known as the deep groove bearing. Plain ball races, roller and needle roller bearings are not usually suitable. Taper roller bearings would be ideal, except that they only work one way. As soon as you go astern, everything will fall to pieces - you need a pair of these, facing in opposite directions. Bearings specifically designed for end loads (thrust races) often cannot take side loads, so another bearing is again needed.

Ball bearings are usually grease lubricated, and as long as they are protected from water and dirt, and not overloaded, are virtually maintenance free.

The thrust bearing must be securely anchored to the shaft so that it cannot slide along it either way. Lots of methods are possible, but remember that the shaft has to be put into the tube from the outside (usually), and the bearing has then to be put onto it from inside. A simple way is the taper-lock bush. Other arrangements might involve turned shoulders, collars or locknuts.

Close astern of the thrust block is the gland. The function of this is to keep the water out of the boat. The bearing nearest the propeller is usually water lubricated and the shaft tube is flooded. The inner end of the tube is sealed to the shaft by the gland. It is often considered desirable for the gland to leak slightly - at least this shows that it is not too tight. The gland seems to need much more attention than the thrust block.

56. **TRAILERS I: RULES**

We, with trailable boats, all have intimate knowledge and take considerable trouble over their working. However, how many of us are knowledgable of the regulations regarding our trailers?

A number of members had problems with trailers last year, so we felt it was appropriate to deal with regulations and maintenance.

Let's first look at the legal requirements, dealing only with trailers up to 3.5 tonnes gross trailer weight (since above this weight the regulations differ widely). These notes do not cover all the legal requirements in detail but are an indication of the general requirements for the assistance of members. The rules change from time to time; the full details are contained in the latest "Construction and Use" and "Road Vehicle Lighting" regulations, available from HM Stationery Office. Revised regulations came into force in October 1982 to improve the safety of all *new* trailers.

Definitions:

Unladen Weight: weight of trailer including all fittings but excluding the removable load it is designed to carry.

Gross Trailer Weight: the total unladen weight of the trailer *plus* the maximum payload which it is designed to carry.

Kerb Weight: the weight of the vehicle, including full fuel and water tanks and all necessary lubricants, spare wheel, loose tools and other items normally supplied with the vehicle, but excluding driver, passengers and their luggage.

Close-coupled Trailer: a two axle trailer with the wheel centres on each side less than 1 metre apart. Close-coupled axles are considered as one axle.

Trailer Plate:

Trailers below 1020 kg unladen weight must be permanently marked, on the near side in a prominent position, with the *gross* trailer weight. Trailers above 1020 kg must have a prescribed Ministry Plate fitted to the near side.

Unbraked Trailers:

Trailers of less than 2 cwt unladen weight were allowed to be braked but, after October 1986, unbraked trailers are only allowed if they are under 750 kg *gross* weight. They must also be less than half the towing vehicle's kerb weight.

Braked Trailers:

All trailers made after October 1982 must comply with the new regulations, but these are not retrospective. New trailers must have brakes achieving 45%g efficiency; this can only be met with purpose-built cable/rod operated brakes with a **hydraulic** damped coupling. To date it has not been possible to design an all hydraulic system. Hence this rules out the use of reclaimed car hubs as these can only be used through the handbrake system and this would not achieve 45%g.

Where trailers are fitted with more than one axle, brakes are required on all wheels. A parking brake must be fitted to all braked trailers, to operate on at least two road wheels on each axle, and capable of being maintained by direct mechanical (rod or cable) action.

Dimensions:

The normal maximum length for a 2 wheel trailer is 7 metres excluding draw-bar and coupling. This can be increased to 12 metres when the trailer has not less than 4 wheels, the centres of which are not less than $\frac{3}{5}$ ths of the overall length and the total vehicle exceeds 2030 kg unladen weight. (Powered braking systems are required on such trailers.)

The maximum allowable width is 2.3 m (but 2.5 m if the towing vehicle exceeds 2030 kg unladen weight), but must not extend more than 305 mm beyond each side of the towing vehicle - irrespective of allowable width.

Tyres and Wheels:

It is illegal to mix radial and cross-ply tyres on a trailer; it is also recommended that for greater safety they should be of the same type as those on the towing vehicle. Many industrial and agricultural tyres are only suitable for slow speeds and hence are not suitable for our purposes.

When using reclaimed wheels and/or tyres, it is necessary to check with the manufacturers regarding their loading suitability.

Mudguards must be fitted to the rear wheels of all trailers (both sets on twin axle trailers) unless the body of the trailer affords adequate protection against any mud and water thrown up.

Couplings:

Since October 1982, spring overrun couplings must not be fitted to any new trailer, as they do not usually comply with the braking standards now required. A hydraulically damped unit and overrun, to the latest EEC directive 71/320 must be used, which must be designed and approved for at least the gross weight of the trailer.

A 50 mm ball coupling will normally be used (old 2" couplings are no longer recommended) together with a 50 mm ball hitch which may have a small flat on top and may be stamped "ISO 50 mm". A wide range of towing eyes may also be used and must be matched by an appropriate towing jaw or hook fitted to the towing vehicle.

There should in all cases be a positive nose weight (usually between 25 and 100 kg), to help create stable towing conditions and reduce coupling wear, but this weight must never exceed the towing vehicle's recommended limits.

An emergency break-away cable must be fitted to the hand brake linkage with the other end fitted to the vehicle. Alternatively, safety chains can be used up to 1500 kg gross trailer weight, and these must be short enough to prevent the front end from striking the road surface.

Lighting:

All trailer lighting units must carry the European 'E' or 'e' marking showing that they comply with the performance standards. Lamp requirements are summarised in the table shown.

TRAILERS: TABLE OF LIGHTING REGULATIONS

	Maximum distance from edge	Distance from ground		Comments
		Min	*Max*	
Two direction indicator lamps, Category 2, with amber lenses	400 mm	350 mm	1500 mm	If it is not possible to meet this height requirement, this dimension may be increased to 2300 mm on post 1/4/86 trailers but only up to 2100 mm on pre-1/4/86
Two stop lamps with red lenses	No max, but minimum separation 400 mm	350 mm	1500 mm	Ditto
Two tail lamps at rear with red lenses	400 mm	350 mm	1500 mm	Or up to 2100 mm on post 1/10/85 trailers if necessary
One rear fog lamp with red lens (only mandatory on trailers over 1.3 m wide)	None stated but minimum separation	250 mm	1500 mm	Two lamps preferred, but if only one, must be to offside of centreline of trailer
Two red triangular reflectors*	400 mm	350 mm	900 mm	On post 1/10/85 trailers this can be increased to 1200 mm if structure requires this.
For trailers built after October 1985 and more than 1.6 m wide, front side lights are compulsory:	150 mm	none	1500 mm	If this is not possible, this can be increased to 1200 mm

* NB Trailers pulled by goods vehicles over 2 tonnes unladen weight must be fitted with two triangular reflectors with white surrounds in the same positions stated above.

57. **TRAILERS II: MAINTENANCE**

Most trailers are made from tubular steel, very often with seals at the ends, and if the frame appears to be free from corrosion outside one hopes that this will also be true of the inside. All too often this is proved not to be the case when a member actually breaks in service (very nasty) or the chipping hammer falls through on the rare occasion when a repaint is thought necessary. These shocks are very easy to avoid. On a new trailer proceed as follows; on an old one check the soundness of the frames with firm hammer blows all over before starting. First drill and tap approximately ¼" drain holes at the rear bottom extremity of each frame. Do likewise at the front and top of each member. Don't be surprised if water runs out. If it does, set the trailer at a steep angle and leave it to drain in the sun or a warm garage; alternatively a little heat from a blow lamp would not come amiss. When dried out plug the bottom holes with screws and jointing compound and with a large oil can put a tea cup of old sump oil in each tube and seal the filler hole with a screw. This will wash around inside when the trailer is in motion and greatly prolong the life of the tube. Go through the same exercise each year and your trailer will outlast the boat. Even if the frames are open ended it is worth pushing an oily rag through them or better still fitting them with wooden bungs and putting oil in them as above.

Trailer Lights

Who hasn't been all ready to go with the trailer attached only to find that the trailer lights don't work, or that you have borrowed a trailer and any but the right lights come on when you do a test? Always waggle the plug in its socket for a moment or two, then test again. Next check that all the bulbs are sound. Assuming that your car has been wired to standard (if not, in your own interests make sure that it is) then any equipment that you buy, hire or borrow should work.

Standard Connections for Trailer Sockets:-

Pin No.	Wire colour	Function
1	Yellow	Nearside Indicator
2	Blue	Fog Light
3	White	Earth
4	Green	Offside Indicator
5	Brown	Offside Tail & Front
6	Red	Stop Lights
7	Black	Nearside Tail, Front & No. Plate Lights

58. **TRAILERS III - STABILITY**

If you tow a fairly heavy boat with your car, the following points may be of help:

(a) The trailer weight distribution should be balanced to give about 100-130 lb downward thrust on the ball;

(b) Stowage of fuel and water in the boat can be used to achieve this. Alternatively, it may be necessary to alter the position of the boat on the trailer;

(c) With a four-wheel trailer, fine tuning can be done by adjusting the tyre pressure of the forward or aft pair of wheels.

When you get the right adjustment, the improvement in stability can be astonishing and it is certainly worth the effort, if only for the sake of safety.

A caravan type stabiliser is also worth considering if you have an adverse weight ratio to contend with.

59. **TUBE BENDING**

The Light Steam Power water-tube boiler is of Illingworth configuration and is fired by a paraffin vapourising burner of Lune Valley type. It is stated to be suitable for a 20' launch. Whether it is good, bad or indifferent I do not know because I have not yet steamed it. This account describes no more than my efforts to find, bend and fit suitable tubing.

An unsolicited paper received with the drawings, being an account of the experiences of one maker of this boiler, reads in part as follows:

"After unsuccessfully trying to bend the ½" bore copper tubes to the shape specified in the drawings, and not being able to find anyone who could do so, I made them of simple 'C' shape with horizontal ends".

This admission, sent to me with the drawings by their owner, and suggesting a need to curtail the heating surface and sacrifice some compactness, was not very encouraging. But other discouragements were to follow; the boiler tubing specified by the drawings is " ½" bore 18 gauge domestic copper water tubing". I daresay Noah plumbed his ark with this, but it has not been available off the shelf for many a long year. That now available is 15 mm OD and only half the thickness of 18 gauge.

Depressed, I consoled myself with the idea that it would be logical to attempt the burner first before worrying about procuring and bending suitable boiler tube - because if bending the vapourising coil were to prove beyond me, there would be no point in attempting the boiler tubes at all. Part of the instructions for bending the vapourising tube reads:

"Solid-drawn mild steel tube ½" OD by 13 gauge, 1½ turns of flat

Figure 1

spiral coil and thence into an inverted cone with a minimum of 3¼"

I got this considered by a professional tube manipulating specialist with a South Coast reputation, who announced that it was impossible.

By now I had become thoroughly demoralised over the whole thing, but before consigning the drawings to the WPB, I telephoned Sam Wilkinson. He was good enough to instruct me what tubing to buy and how to bend the 'Beehive' shape shown in Figure 1, as follows: the idea of 13 gauge was nonsense. I needed three metres of very thick-walled soft mild steel high pressure hydraulic tubing. At least half the OD to be wall thickness, because the 'beehive' had to be bent cold, and anything less thick-walled would kink. Eventually, after some interesting failures, I found a supplier prepared to obtain for me my very small order of just one 6 metre length of BS 980 mild steel tube, ½" OD by 10 gauge.

A conical aluminium winding former was cast. This was drilled for the "pressure tank to vapouriser" 1½ ft of tubing - see Figure 2.

The "small diameter" end-opening of this tube hole had to be faired and rounded considerably by hammering on an old wood gouge (ruined in the process) to accommodate the sharpest bendable 90° change of direction of the remainder of the 3 metres to be wound. This first sharp bend, and several others after the formation of the 'beehive' all required the intense heat of a borrowed mini oxy-acetylene outfit. It will be appreciated that the tube end presented to the reader's eye in Figure 2 was, in fact, more than eight feet away from the winding

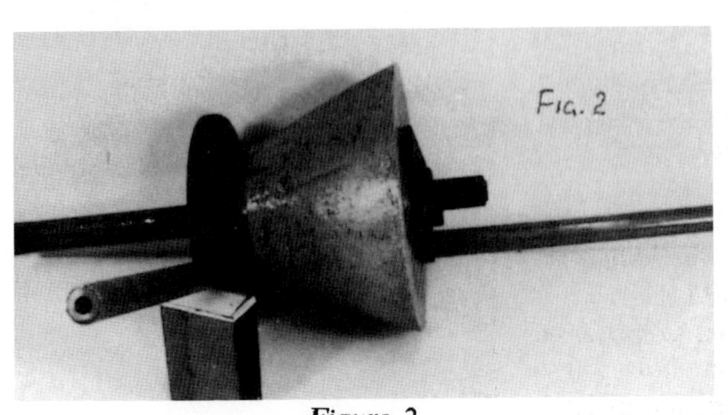

Figure 2

former before commencement of winding, but this cannot be shown in close-up photography. What is apparent from this tube-end photo is that the wall thickness of this ½" OD tube is just over an eighth of an inch. The loaded winding former was taken, on a roof rack, to a 6" lathe and revolved at the lowest possible speed. Remarkably easily the one and a half turns of flat spiral coil were formed and the tube then climbed the revolving cone.

I then began thinking about 18 gauge copper tubing. Because a bending machine (or parts of one) would be required, the OD had to be 15 mm. A "Record" bending machine seemed both expensive and unsuitable. For one thing, the quadrant embodied was for some reason considerably less than the 180° I required. But the manager of the engineers' tool concern became interested, went and rummaged in his spare parts department and found a 15 mm spare part former of 180°, also a spare 15 mm follower. These I bought and constructed my own bending machine (Figure 3) around them. Why a 180° former is not fitted in a standard bending machine I do not know.

Now I was in a position to bend the right size of copper tube. From a job I once did I remembered having used a wonderful little tube-drawing firm at an obscure location near Poole. They manufactured for me sufficient 15 mm by 18 gauge copper tube (in maximum roof-rack lengths) for little more than I would have to pay for the quite useless plumbers' piping from a builders' merchant. Their particulars, and those of my

Figure 3

supplier of just one length of ½" OD 10 gauge steel tube, have been submitted for inclusion in the next *Suppliers Directory*.

The one peculiar tube (the one on the extreme right) and many of the 31 ordinary boiler tubes are visible in Figure 4. The peculiar tube is required because it has to miss the welded-in branch for the bottom of the gauge glass (which will be well in the fire) by a sufficient distance to allow this branch to be heavily lagged. Freehand bending of this odd tube caused more difficulty than the machine bending of any of the uniform 31. Figure 5 shows the completion of the last bending operation of the three bends required for each standard tube. Before bending, each of the 29½" long copper tubes was annealed. The strong ¼" tab on the bending machine is for securing the thing in a vice.

The single vertical drum is a 6" ID, 6½" OD MS seamless tube 21" high. This was placed on a piece of ¼" plywood across the ways of my unfortunate Myford ML7 lathe, and pushed by the tailstock against a $\frac{37}{64}$" drill in the headstock. The

Figure 4

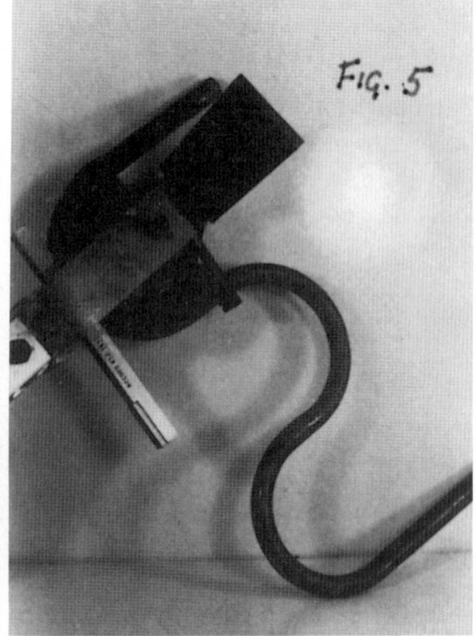

Figure 5

resulting 32 top and 32 bottom holes were then finished with a 15 mm hand reamer. The 32 bent tubes received their final annealing and the end centres were adjusted to exactly 12½" apart in a jig. They entered their holes fairly tightly but without trouble.

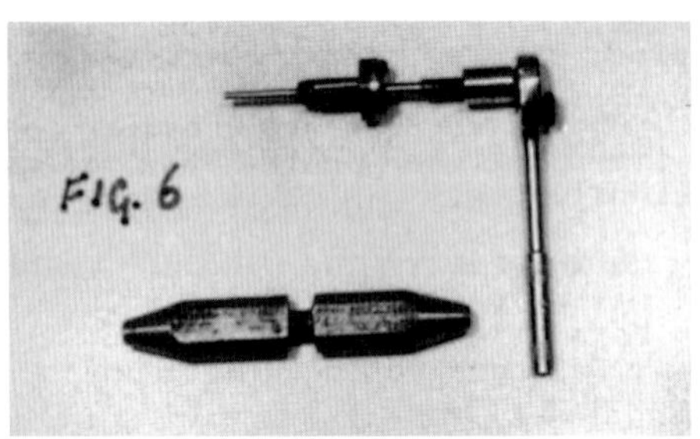

Figure 6

The Wicksteed E4P expander, with miniature ratchet lever, can be seen in Figure 6. At the bottom end of the drum, where the tube holes are only 1" and 2" away from the open bottom end, the expanding operation was fairly easy; but at the top end, with the tube centres 6½" and 7½" away from the end, it was not. A wooden backer-up had to be used in this fiddle, with a blunted wood screw pressing into the dimple on the end of the ratchet axis.

Wicksteed do have 15 mm belling expanders, but not as small as this. I therefore made one up out of hexagon bar, using a fine thread (26 tpi) and 15 mm tapered and truncated ends. All tube ends were painted with blue marking where they entered the drum. fitting the tapered ends of the jack into the already expanded ends of two diametrically opposed tubes, I screwed them up hard with a pair of spanners. A careful watch was kept on the blue marking, but mercifully no tube end shifted under the considerable outward pressure, and the tool had done a good belling job.

60. **TWIST DRILLS**

Drill sharpening is often seen as a black art not to be attempted by the uninitiated. It is an art well worth teaching yourself because it will save hours of frustration. Forget the gadgets on the market that cannot do an effective job.

Three basic rules apply:

(a) The angle at the point of the drill should be 120°. Cut a small piece of sheet metal to this angle as a handy gauge to use while learning the art.

(b) Imagine the drill in the hole against the surface which it is cutting. Only the cutting edge should be in contact. An angular clearance should be developed behind it of between 10° and 20°, reducing with increasing drill size. Below 3° it will not cut; if it is too great, it will cut too fiercely.

(c) The point must be symmetrical in angle and width. Errors in this respect will make the drill cut oversize, usually leaving a small diameter lip where the drill emerges from the far side of a through hole.

Thus oversize holes can be produced when required by grinding an offset point on a drill.

If you want to avoid the step at the end of the hole, simply drill through into a piece of scrap backing metal.

Only practice makes perfect. Get an old drill about ¼" to ⅛" in diameter and regrind it a dozen times.

Each time check it:

(a) Against your 120° gauge. hold it up to the light; is the angle right? Is there sufficient relief?

(b) Drill a piece of mild steel and a piece of brass not less than ¼" thick. Is the hole accurate to size?

With practice, it will become second nature - like riding a bicycle!

* * * *

Instead of making a gauge, simply place two nuts of the same size together and - hey presto - you have a 120° included angle.

The drill can now be checked with ease. (I always lose little drill gauges and the like!)

61. VALVE GEAR

Purpose:

To open and close the valve at the appropriate times during the piston motion, and to provide a means of reversing the engine.

Principle:

The Stephenson Link valve gear (figure 1) is probably the most

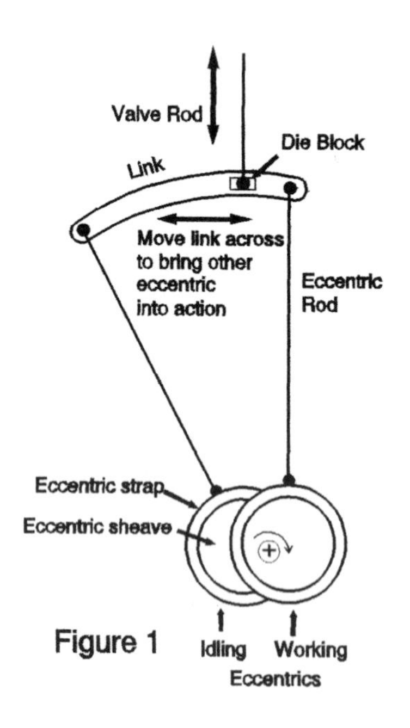

Figure 1

common one on small boats. This has two eccentrics (disks rotating with the crankshaft, but mounted off centre). One of them has its maximum position before that of the piston when the engine is running ahead, the other when it is running astern. The motion of one or the other is transmitted to the valve by a die block in a curved slotted link. The link can be moved so that the die block is at either end of it, or somewhere in between. When the die block is in the centre of the link, the valve is held stationary in mid position, and the engine stops.

Two other types of valve gear are often found on small boats. The Hackworth only has one eccentric, and an inclined slider. If it is inclined one way, the engine goes ahead, the other way gives astern, and flat stops the engine. The Joy is similar to the Hackworth, but takes its motion from the connecting rod instead of an eccentric.

Operation:

In most situations, engines are happiest in or near *full link* - i.e. at one extreme of the travel. Economy can sometimes be improved by *linking up* a little, but this is not nearly so effective in steam boats as in land vehicles. A railway locomotive can vary its power independently of speed (e.g. by going downhill), and good control of the link can be beneficial. A boat, however, generally has a fixed relationship between power and speed. Boats can't coast downhill (although a following wind or an auxiliary sail, but not the tide, might give a similar effect).

It is not usually a good idea to move the reversing gear while the throttle is open, since the steam pressure holding the stationary valve against its face will lead to excessive friction, and the sudden release of steam into the cylinder will lead to shock loading. In extreme cases, this has been known to fracture propeller shaft couplings, and worse. On the other hand, most small engines are not reliably self-starting (the twin high pressure is the simplest which is), and juggling with the link can often help persuade them. There is not much harm in partly opening the throttle valve before starting the engine by moving the linkwork, then opening up the throttle.

62. **VALVE SETTING I**

Joy, Marshall, Bremme and Hackworth Gears

In the articles in FUNNELs 68, 69 & 71 the information was confined to designs based on Stevenson's Link, because these are by far the most common. They also have the advantage that the functions of the various parts and their adjustments are fairly obvious. Alternative types coming under the general heading *Radial Valve Gears* are not so simple to understand or adjust and questions about them have resulted in this article.

In FUNNELs 32, 33 & 34 the late George Watkins described the four most common types: HACKWORTH, MARSHALL, BREMME and JOY, and for reference his diagrams are reproduced here.

Why the term Radial was adopted has never been explained, because it does not relate to the one feature that occurs in all of the designs. That is taking the thrust from the crankshaft or connecting rod at right angles to the piston rod. This means that in order to have the valve fully open when the piston is approaching a point halfway down the cylinder two alternative activators can be used:

1. A single eccentric, dead in line with the crank. (Note that an advance setting cannot be used because it must be positioned for both ahead and astern operation.) In Bremme & Hackworth it will coincide with the crankpin because the valve rod fulcrum is beyond the suspension point. If it is inside the suspension point, the eccentric will be diametrically opposed to the crankpin, as in the early form of Hackworth & Marshall.

2. A fulcrum point formed on the side of the conrod, carrying a drag link supported at its other end by a suspension link attached to the cylinder. It is the sideways movement that is utilised and the drag link serves to eliminate some of the far greater vertical motion of the crosshead. The valve actuating link is moved by a fulcrum partway along the drag link.

The sideways movement imparted by the eccentric or link is converted to vertical motion in either of the following ways:

(a) A swinging link supported on an arm that can be rotated between the ahead and astern positions, as shown in Marshall, Bremme and some forms of Joy.

(b) A curved or straight slide, mounted on a trunnion at its centre on which it can be rotated to the ahead or astern positions. The joint onto the slide block is also pivoted.

Setting Up

All the levers and cranks may appear to be rather complicated when considering settings. There is a simple approach using two golden rules:

1. When the crank is horizontal, and the gear in neutral (support arm vertical or slide bar horizontal) the centre lines of all the links and rods must be either in line or at right angles to each other. On some engines the suspension links from the cylinder may slope in slightly but if excessive it will complicate the fine adjustment of equal valve sequences in the up and down strokes.

2. When the crank is horizontal, and the gear in neutral a line taken through the centres of the bearings on the links should be straight and horizontal (where an eccentric is used its centre is included).

Equalising Valve Movements

The angular movement of the slide bar or support arm should be set to an equal angle in both directions. This angle should give the total valve travel required.

Set a datum line at the top limit of valve travel, ahead full gear (Position A). Turn engine to bring valve to bottom limit (Position B). Record distance of A from B. Move gear to full astern. Turn to top limit of valve travel (Position C). It should be at the datum line. If not, adjust the position of the support arm or slide trunnion until A & C coincide. Turn engine to full astern bottom valve travel (Position D). Now A to B should be the same distance as C to D. Any discrepancy should be corrected by adjustment of the ahead and astern limit stops. Now the limit stops may be adjusted by equal amounts to set the correct full gear valve travel.

The Valve Settings

The valve lap can be established as in Funnel 69.

Adjust the valve location on its rod to give equal opening top and bottom if obliquity is ignored. If it is to be taken into account, the valve lands will have to be unequal and the valve lifted or dropped from the equal opening position on the rod as instructed in Funnel 69.

Rig a pointer by the flywheel and mark the four opening and closing points ahead on the back edge, and astern on the front edge. Openings should occur just before centres, and closings about 120° after centres. The ahead and astern limit stops may require further slight adjustment to perfect these positions.

Adjustments

Ahead and astern valve travel unequal: adjust the limit stops on the angular movement of the swing link or slide.

Valve functions not symmetrical on up and down stroke: adjust the vertical position of the fulcrum of the swing link or slide bar. When the motion is taken from the conrod, the effective length of the static suspension link can be adjusted as an alternative. A bottle screw adjuster in the link is a good idea for ease of adjustment.

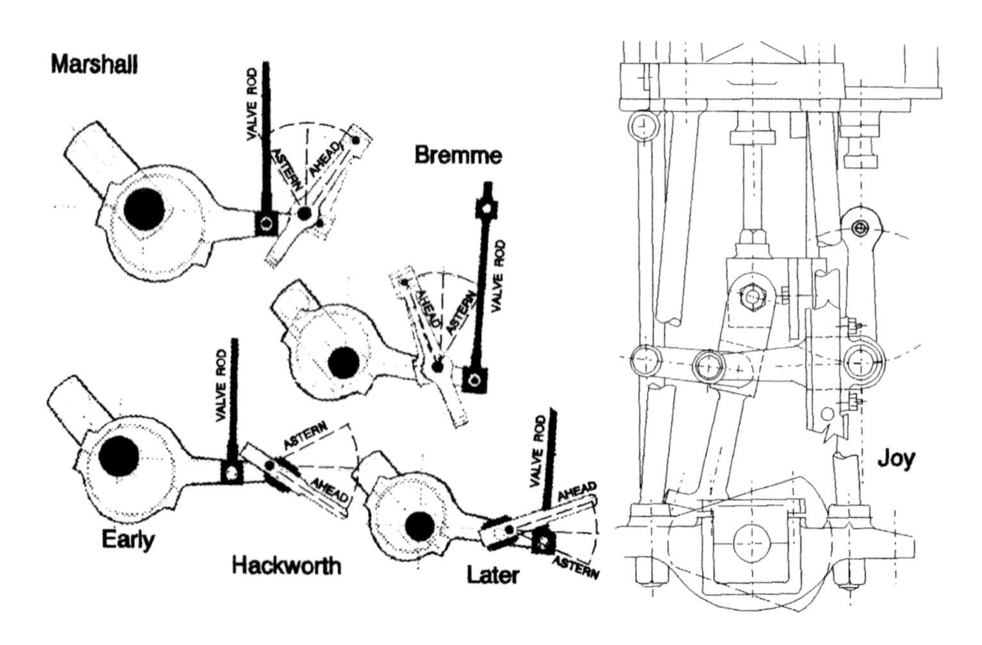

63. VALVE SETTING II

Timing

Marking the flywheel is the only satisfactory way to set the valves of a steam engine. Assuming that they are dimensionally correct:

(a) Permanently mount a pointer adjacent to the flywheel OD.

(b) With a sharp chisel, mark each cylinder top and bottom dead centre, for preference using letter and number stamps.

(c) With a felt tip marker, mark the positions at which the edge of the inlet port just emerges from behind each valve in each direction. It is ideal to have two colours - one for ahead and one for astern.

(d) The valve settings will be correct when the valve opening marks for ahead and astern are an equal distance from their related cylinders' top and bottom dead-centre marks.

Allen Keys for Valve Setting

When setting slide valves it is difficult to measure equal opening at the top and bottom of the slide's travel. One solution is to use a set of unworn Allen keys as slip-gauges. Insert the end of the key in the slot of the exposed port at the top and bottom valve position. Turn the key to take up any clearance. Adjust the valve to achieve the same angular movement at both ends, which indicates equal opening.

64. **VARNISHING**

Varnishing cannot be beaten as a finish. On good woodwork, the following points should be borne in mind if you want to achieve a long-lasting finish:

(a) If the finish of the wood is not smooth and free from defects, do not start;

(b) The best surface is pre-filled marine ply which is ready for varnishing but a little more expensive;

(c) If not pre-filled, rub the surface with a good filler;

(d) Rub down with fine abrasive until a silky finish is obtained;

(e) Select varnish: Marine varnish for all outside brightwork, Polyurethane varnish for inside dry surfaces subject to hard wear;

(f) 8 coats for all outside surfaces, 4 coats for inside cabins;

(g) Do not change the brand half way through the job.

First coat: dilute with 25% white spirit;
24 hours to dry, thoroughly rub down;
Second coat - 12 hours to dry;
Third coat - 24 hours to dry, lightly rub down;
Fourth coat - 12 hours to dry;
Fifth coat - 24 hours to dry, lightly rub down;
Sixth coat - 12 hours to dry;
Seventh coat - 48 hours to dry, rub down to produce a smooth matt surface all over;
Eighth coat - 12 hours to dry.

Always apply varnish fairly thinly - better to miss a bit than have a run.

It's about right when the brush moves easily rather than tending to stick.

Varnishing Teak

Although teak is often used untreated, its grain can be enhanced by varnishing, but its oily nature can present problems. These can be avoided if the work is rubbed down with a rag soaked in dry-cleaning fluid (toluene).

Allow a minute or two for the surface to dry and immediately prime with varnish let down with 25% white spirit. **Warning!** Toluene is anaesthetic - not to be used in a confined space.

65. WATER TREATMENT

This article was prompted by a discussion on whether the small boilers of steam launches may be left filled when not in use, a question which depends very much on the kind of feed water, the water treatment and any possible risk of corrosion. This led to considering what methods of water treatment are necessary for a steam boat in which the boiler feed consists largely of condensate; this reduces the formation of scale but does increase the risk of corrosion. So here then is an engineer's account, in simple terms, of the principal feed water impurities and how to deal with them.

The two main problems are firstly corrosion which could lead to structural weakness and costly repairs, and secondly scale formation on the heating surfaces which increases fuel consumption and in an extreme case could cause damage.

Scale Formation

There are two kinds of water hardness: *temporary hardness* which is precipitated from boiling water to settle as a soft sludge or scale, at the same time releasing carbon dioxide (CO_2) - and *permanent hardness* consisting of soluble salts which precipitate as a hard crystalline scale as soon as their concentration in the boiler exceeds the limits which the water can hold in solution.

Corrosion

This is a far more serious hazard, and it can result from a variety of causes:-

- Atmospheric oxygen and CO_2 dissolved in the feed water;
- Additional CO_2 released when water containing temporary hardness is boiled;
- Natural acidity of some waters, especially very soft waters as indicated by a low pH value. The breakdown of acid-forming salts under boiler working conditions may add to this acidity;
- Ordinary rusting - i.e. oxidation of iron in a damp atmosphere.

Dissolved oxygen absorbed from the air is the most serious of these, causing deep pitting or localised wastage by an electro-chemical action in which areas shielded from the aerated water by a small patch of scale or rust become an anode from which the metal ions escape to the larger cathodic surface. This process, known as *differential aeration* is far more vigourous when using condensate return because hot water absorbs oxygen more readily. Naturally soft waters also have a greater affinity for oxygen. Salinity or other forms of acidity speed up the process by increasing the electrical conductivity of the water.

The second danger comes from CO_2 absorbed from the atmosphere and also from the breakdown of any temporary hardness which is allowed to enter the boiler. This may cause corrosion in the steam spaces and also gives the water a slightly acid reaction resulting in a slow wastage of the metal surfaces. The effect is more pronounced on surfaces swept by flowing water which sometimes causes "grooving" around the base of the shell or firebox. Surface wastage is generally a slow process over a number of years, but is more active in the presence of dissolved oxygen. Other sources of acidity are very soft waters and supplies fed from peat moorland streams or affected by industrial pollution.

Ordinary rusting, or oxidation in a damp atmosphere, is not a very serious matter and has sometimes been regarded as a protection because the initial film slows down and halts a continuation of the process.

Colloidal tannin treatment

Fortunately there is a simple water treatment which is particularly suitable for conditions on a steam launch where the boiler feed may consist largely of very soft condensate return, rich in dissolved oxygen and therefore potentially corrosive. This treatment is a colloidal compound of tannin supplied by Houseman (Burnham) Ltd (formerly Houseman and Thompson), under the trade name of 'D.M. Boiler Enamel'. It has the following properties:

1. A high capacity for absorbing oxygen;
2. In the absence of scale, it forms a protective film of iron tannate on underwater metal surfaces which gives protection against corrosion and is also claimed to repel scale formation;
3. Its colloidal form coagulates the particles of scale as they come out of

solution in the boiler, thus forming a soft sludge which does not settle as scale but can be discharged by blowing down.

4. In addition to preventing scale formation it can, over a long period, loosen and eventually remove existing scale. But if treatment is being introduced in a boiler already heavily scaled it would be better to have it descaled first with inhibited acid.

This D.M. treatment should be applied in the hotwell as close as possible to the injector or feed pump suction pipe. In some moderately soft waters with low acidity the D.M. tannin treatment alone may be sufficient, but for less favourable waters there are two *Conjunctional Treatments* which are similar to the conventional lime-soda process of water softening:

Treatment A: using hydrated lime, reacts with the temporary hardness which then settles as a soft deposit of chalk without releasing any CO_2;

Treatment B: containing soda ash which similarly converts the permanent hardness into a soft deposit of chalk.

Both treatments provide the necessary alkalinity for counteracting acidity.

The corrosive effect of acidity is neutralised by adding alkalinity to increase the pH value of the water to a minimum of pH 10 (pH 7.0 is neutral, lower figures are acid, higher figures alkaline). Treatment A for temporary hardness should be used in the make-up tank and in sufficient quantity to give pH 10.

Treatment B for permanent hardness should be applied in the hotwell close to the injector of feed pump suction pipe, also in sufficient quantities to maintain pH 10.

If the removal of the permanent and temporary hardness is not completed before the feedwater enters the boiler, the particles of chalk precipitated in the boiler will be coagulated by the tannin treatment in the manner already described, and any acidity from the additional CO_2 gas will be neutralised by the pH 10 alkalinity.

Thus all the undesirable and dangerous water impurities are dealt with by the combination of the D.M. tannin and its conjunctional treatments as summarised below:

(a) The corrosive dissolved oxygen is absorbed by the tannin compound;

(b) The corrosive influence of CO_2 and of soft waters or hot condensate return is neutralised by the alkalinity of the conjunctional treatments A or B;

(c) The protective film of iron tannate repels both scale formation and the different corrosive attacks;

(d) Temporary and permanent hardness are reduced by the conjunctional treatments;

(e) The formation of scale from any hardness which enters the boiler is prevented by the coagulant properties of the tannin treatment.

One other minor trouble is foaming or *priming* which causes a carry-over of water in the wet steam. this results from an excessive accumulation of solids in suspension which are precipitated when the boiler water is unable to hold any more in solution. Such excessive concentrations should be avoided by occasionally blowing down a small quantity of boiler water at the end of a working day, sufficient to ensure that the water in the gauge glass does not become clouded. With some supplies of water this may be necessary every time the boiler is used.

Boiler out of Service

The boiler should preferably be left empty when out of use during the winter to avoid frost damage and for the purpose of inspection and maintenance. The pressure gauge should be kept indoors as it may become inaccurate and unreliable if allowed to freeze. Empty the boiler after cooling it down slowly, after which it can be dried out with a small fire of wood chips in the firebox. brush down any carbon deposits from the firebox, tubes and funnel uptake, and exclude damp air by closing ashpan dampers and shrouding the burner air intake.

For shorter periods of shut down during the season there should be no need to empty the boiler providing it has been receiving regular water treatment. Before dropping steam, the boiler should be given a moderate overdose of the tannin treatment together with the additional alkalinity to raise its pH value to not less than 11. The risk of corrosion will then be no greater when the boiler is idle than when it is working; in fact, the risk from dissolved oxygen may be even less because the water is not continually receiving fresh injections of soft and aerated hot condensate.

The only exception to this is that the boiler should always be left empty when idle for short periods if the feedwater contains a large proportion of what is known as *Greensand Water*. This water can cause highly aggressive corrosion unless blended with less harmful supplies; it occurs in some bore-holes of the Thames valley area and the water authority may be able to say which supplies, if any, may be seriously affected.

Finally, I hope I have not painted too alarming a picture of the hazards of corrosion; these are largely based on normal experience with boilers which are in service almost every day of the year for years on end. The risks are correspondingly less for boilers which are only steamed occasionally, but please do not neglect the tannin treatment and always maintain pH 10 while the boiler is working, with pH 11 as an extra safeguard when it is idle.

66. **WHISTLE AND SIREN**

Purpose:

To make a loud noise when required, primarily for signalling to other craft.

Principle:

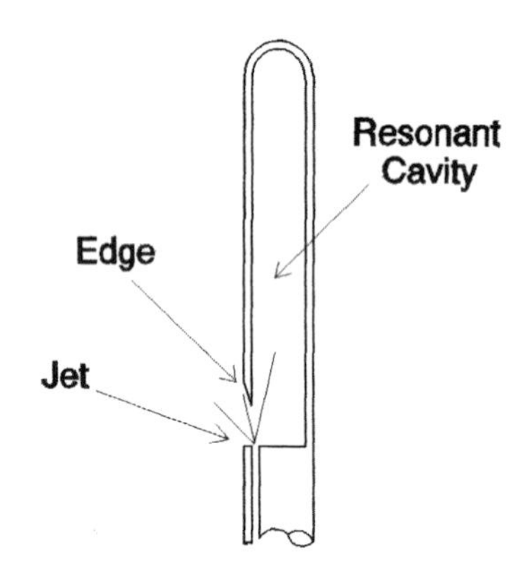

Figure 1 - The Whistle

When a high-speed jet of fluid strikes a sharp edge, it tends to oscillate from one side to another in an unstable and unpredictable manner. If there is a resonant cavity nearby (like an organ pipe), the resonant frequency of the cavity will force the frequency of the fluid oscillation. This is the principle of many musical instruments as well as organs and the steam whistle (figure 1).

The siren works by a rather different method. A jet of steam is directed to a spinning plate with

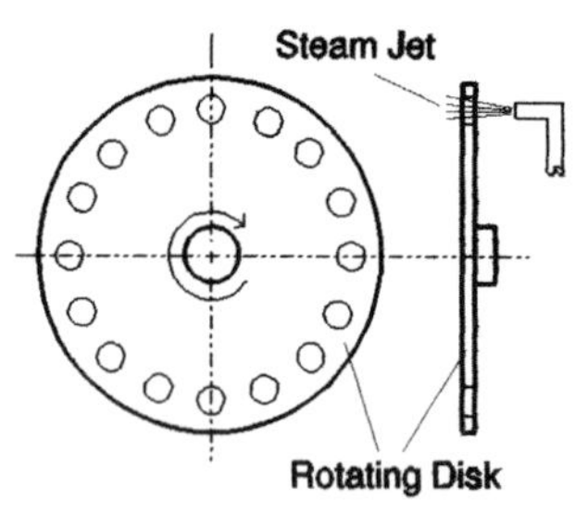

Figure 2 - The Siren

holes in. The jet is alternately let through the holes and obstructed. Now you hear it; now you don't. If the disc spins fast enough, the interruption is at a high enough frequency to produce a musical (?) note (figure 2). The disc is usually powered by some form of steam turbine.

Operation:

Both the whistle and the siren like their steam to be dry; droplets of water spoil the effect. This means that it is preferable to keep them hot, otherwise time and steam are wasted every time they are used. I keep **SENTA**'s whistle hot by mounting it directly on top of the boiler. Another way is to run the whistle pipe inside the funnel. A third is to keep it well lagged, and allow a continuous slow leak of steam through it (which often is the case more by accident than design, anyway).

Remember that the prime purpose of the whistle is signalling (see 'How Steamboaters Do It' in Part 1). Avoid any possibility of anyone else being misled by your signals. I seem to remember a tale of someone being arrested for using a siren in Portsmouth Harbour - apparently that is a right reserved to the Royal Navy. Moral - watch out for local rules.

67. **WINCH LINE**

If you find just *one* strand broken in your winch wire, replace it without delay. The end of a strand can cause terrible finger injury; the whiplash effect of this wire breaking under tension when launching could be lethal, not to mention damage to your boat. Most marinas or chandlers dealing with yacht rigging will make them up for you.

68. **WOODSCREWS - LUBRICATION**

When building **SAUMAREZ**, I estimated that I drove more than 1000 woodscrews into mahogany and teak. All the screws were brass or bronze and the breakage rate was 1 in 4, almost regardless of size and the drilling of a root diameter hole to take the screws.

By chance I found that rubbing the thread of the screws with Rozalex barrier cream actually eliminated the problem. It is based on soap and, unlike grease, does not stain the wood or affect the adhesion of the varnish.

INDEX

air,
    mixture 26
    pump 13, 35, 70
    supply 11
ALDEBARAN 64
anchor 3
    warp 3
annealing 39-40
anthracite 31
area, heating 9
atmospheric engine 70

ball valves 98
bearers, engine 65
bearing,
    bushes, split 4
    propeller shaft 93
    thrust 93
belt,
    drive 49
    toothed 50
    vee 50
bend, wet 82
bending copper pipes 40
BERYL 62
bevel gear 49
bilge,
    ejector 44
    keel 5
bituminous coal 30
blast pipe 44
blow down valve 21
blower 11-12, 20, 44, 121
boiler,
    corrosion 76, 103
    design 6, 16
    difficulties 29
    drum 7
    energy stored in 6
    flash 7
    horizontal 7
    inspection 15
    laying up 76, 160
        long term 76
        short term 76
    locomotive 7
    Merryweather 7
    monotube 6
    multi-tube 7
    operation 16
    preparation 16
    pressure tests 104
    safety 102, 120
    shell 7
    size 8, 19-20, 65
    tube bending 144
    types 6
    vertical 7
    water level 6
    water tube 7
Bourdon gauge 82
bow,
    clipper 64
    straight 64
brass polishing 23
Bremme valve gear 152
bronze polishing 23
Bunsen burner 43
buoys 116
burgee 52
burner,
    Bunsen 43

Lune Valley 26
oil 24
bushes, bearing 4

cables, steering 132
calibration, pressure gauge 82
casting off 115
centre drill 42
centrifugal pump 97
chain drive 49
channel marks 110, 116
chatter, lathe 75
check valve 13
check list 28
children 81
clack valve 13
clinker 31
coal 30
anthracite 31
bituminous 30
firing 20
fuel 10
hards 31
house 30
lignite 30
semi-anthracite 31
steam, Welsh 31
sub-bituminous 31
types 30
Coalite 31
cocks,
test 18, 55
try 55
water gauge 55
compatibility, chemical 72
compound,
engine 36-37, 45
compounding 37
condensation 76
condenser 35, 70
internal 70
keel 70
purpose 70
vacuum 36
conduction 24
consumption, steam 8
convection 9, 24
copper pipes,
bending 40
joining 40
work hardening 39
corrosion,
boiler 76, 103
stainless steel 131
couplings,
flexible 49
trailer 139
courtesy, ensign 52
cuts, interrupted 75
cylinder,
HP 45
IP 45
LP 45

D, valve 125
damper 11, 20-21, 121
design, boiler 16
detection, gas 86
diaphragm, pump 97
difficulties, boiler 29
dimensions, trailer 138

displacement, pump 97
double acting engine 45
draught 121
drill,
    centre 42
    sharpening, twist 149
drilling thin metal 42
drive,
    belt 49
    chain 49
drum, boiler 7
dry steam 12
dryer, steam 12
dryness fraction 12

eccentric 47
    slip 47
efficiency, mechanical 48
ejector 43
    bilge 44
ELIDIR 8, 92
emulsion paint 51, 74
engine 45, 94
    atmospheric 70
    compound 36-37, 45
    double acting 45
    inverted 45
    oscillating 45
    power, estimation 47
    quadruple expansion 37
    reciprocating 45
        construction 45
    size 65, 94
    triple expansion 37, 45
engine driven pump 18-19
ensign,
    courtesy 52
    red 52
exhaust pipe 71
expansion ratio 37
explosions, causes 16
extractor pump 70

feed,
    pipe 71
    pump 13
fire at sea 110
fire appliances, regulations 108
fire extinguishers 100-1, 110
FIREFLY 7, 127
firing rate 20
fittings, safety 105
flag, saluting 52
flags 52, 117
flame 25
flap valves 98
flash boiler 7
flexible couplings 49
former, pipe bending 40
fuel,
    jet 26
    liquid 24
    pressure 25-26
    safety 106
    solid 24
    temperature 25-26
    vapour 24-25
fuels 9-11
funnel, double skin 73
fusible plug 14

gas,
- detection 86
- fuel 11

gauge,
- Bourdon 82
- calibration, pressure 82
- pressure 14, 82
- vacuum 14
- water level 14, 54

gauge glass 14
- guard 54
- protector 14, 17
- replacement 17, 56
- safety 100, 105
- seals 56

gear, bevel 49
gearbox 49
gland 93, 136
- propeller shaft 93

GRP,
- fixings 57
- hull 57

guard, gauge glass 54

Hackworth valve gear 150, 152
hand pump 18
hardness, water 157
heat transfer 24
heat-resisting paint 51
heating,
- area 9
- surface 24

HERACLES 45
Homefire 31
hook, mooring 58
horizontal boiler 7
house coal 30
Housewarm 32
hull 61
- capacity 62
- material 63
- shape 64
- size 61
- speed 62
- tenderness 66

hydraulic test 104
hydrodynamic pump 97

immersion heater, steam 67
injector 13, 18, 43, 68
- installation 72
- operation 69
- principle 68

inspection, boiler 15
installation, plant 70
interrupted cuts 75

JAMES WATT 49
jet,
- fuel 26
- pump 43

joint,
- palm 41
- universal 49

Joy valve gear 152

keel cooler 35
keel, bilge 5
kettle, Windermere 67
KITTIWAKE 61
knots 114

lagging 72, 74
lathe chatter 75
LAUGHING WATER 64
launching 113, 127
laying up boiler 76, 160
LEO 62
level, water 14
life saving appliances,
    regulations 108
lifebuoys 109
LIGHTNING 62
lignite coal 30
Linda 33
line,
    mooring 58
    winch 164
link 150
linking up 150
liquid fuel 24
locomotive boiler 7
lord, noble 128
Lune Valley burner 26

magic 13
maintenance, propeller 95
man overboard 110
manifold, steam 72
MARIAMNE 127
marks, channel 110
Marshall valve gear 47, 152
materials,
    modern 73
    traditional 73
mechanical efficiency 48
Merryweather boiler 8
metal, drilling thin 42
mixture, air 26
monotube boiler 6
mooring 113
    hook 58
    line 58
MORVEN 62
mud drum 7
mudbanks 110
MUDLARK 48, 62
multi-tube boiler 7

NATALIE 127
navigation rules 116, 118
non-return valve 13

oil,
    separation 70
    separator, hot well 59
oil firing 20
    rules 78
oil fuel 11
operation, boiler 16
oscillating engine 45
OXBIRD 127

paint,
    emulsion 51
    heat-resisting 51
palm joint 41
passengers 79, 115
    behaviour 79
    helpful 80
    regulations 108
Phurnacite 31
pipe,
    bending, former 40

blast 44
exhaust 71
feed 71
steam 71
pipes, copper, work hardening 39
pipework 70
materials 71
safety 104
piston pump 97
pitch, propeller 91
plant installation 70
plug, fusible 14
plunger pump 97
polishing,
brass 23
bronze 23
Porta's gas producer 32-32
precautions, propane 87
pressure,
fuel 25-26
gauge 14, 82
calibration 82
priming 55
propane,
bottle storage 88
burner 89
firing 83
installation,
British Standard 83, 88
pipework 84, 89
precautions 87
propeller 91
maintenance 95
pitch 91
power 94
shaft 91, 93
bearings 93
gland 93
size 65, 91
slip 92-93
speed 92
propulsion 91
protector, gauge glass 14
puffer 20
puffing 70
pump 97
air 13, 35, 70
centrifugal 97
diaphragm 97
displacement 97
engine driven 18-19
extractor 70
feed 13
hand 18
hydrodynamic 97
jet 43
piston 97
plunger 97
vacuum 43

quadruple expansion engine 37
QUEEN MARY 63
quenching 40

radiation 9, 24
ratio, speed/length 63
reamers 99
red ensign 52
red line 14
regulations,
fire appliances 108
life saving appliances 108

passengers 108
regulator 14
relief valve 110
Rexco 31
risk reduction 102
River Esk 33
rules,
  navigation 116, 118
  trailers 137
rules of road 116

safety 100
  at sea 110
  boiler 102, 120
  fittings 105
  fuel 106
  gauge glass 100-5
  pipework 104
  steam pipe 101
  studs 101
  valve 14, 19, 111
    dead weight 111
    spring 111
    vent 72
  whistles 106
sandbanks 110
saturated steam 12
SAUMAREZ 45, 51, 63, 95, 110, 128, 165
scale 157
seals, gauge glass 56
seamanship 113
semi-anthracite 31
SENTA 44, 48-49, 64, 72, 162
separator,
  oil 59
  steam 12
SERENA 127
setting radial valve 152
sharpening twist drill 149
shell boiler 7
shoes, unsuitable 80
signals, whistle 119
silver solder 40, 123
simpling valve 48
SIOUX 62
siren 162
SIRIUS 6 62
skeg 93
slide valve 125
slip, propeller 92-93
slipping, rules 129
slipstream 91
slipways 127
smoke production 33
Smoke Control Area 31
Smokeless Zone 31
solder, silver 40, 123
solid fuel 24
SOOTY 62-63, 127
Spanish windlass 130
speed, hull 62
speed/length ratio 63, 94
spline 49
Split Bearing Bushes 4
springs, mooring 113
stainless steel, corrosion 131
steam,
  accumulation 112
  consumption 8
  dry 12
  dryer 12

immersion heater 67
pipe 71
saturated 12
separator 12
superheated 12
turbine 45
wet 12
steam coal, Welsh 31
steam drum 7
steam generator 7
steam pipe, safety 101
steering cables 132
Stephenson valve gear 150
stern,
canoe 64
counter 64
transom 64
stop valve 14, 72
strainer 72
Stuart Turner 'Cygnet' engine 48
stud driving 133
sub-bituminous coal 31
Sunbrite 31
superheated steam 12
surface, heating 24

taps,
broken 134
new 134
temperature, fuel 25-26
test,
cocks 18, 55
hydraulic 104
threttle valve 14
thrust bearing 93
thrust block 135
toothed belt 50
trailer 127
boat 61
brakes 138
coupling, hydraulic 138
couplings 139
dimensions 138
lights 139-42
maintenance 141
rules 137
stability 143
wheels 138
transfer, heat 24
treatment, water 157
triple expansion engine 37, 45
try cock 55
tube bending 144
turbine, steam 45
TURBINIA 45
twist drill sharpening 149

universal joint 49

vacuum pump 43
vacuum gauge 14
valve,
ball 98
blow down 21
check 13
clack 13
D 125
flap 98
gear 150
Hackworth 150
Stephenson 150
link 47

non-return 13, 72
pump 98
relief 110
safety 14, 19, 111
vent 72
setting 155
radial 152
simpling 48
slide 125
stop 14, 72
throttle 14
valve gear 45
adjustment 154
Bremme 152
Hackworth 47, 152
Joy 47, 152
Marshall 47, 152
Stephenson 47
vapour, fuel 24-25
varnishing 156
teak 156
vee belt 50
vent, safety valve 72
vertical boiler 7

warts on propeller 95
water,
gauge, testing 16-17
hardness 157
level 14, 16
boiler 6
gauge 14, 54
treatment 157
water gauge, cocks 55
water tube boiler 7
weed hatch 64
Welsh steam coal 31
wet,
bend 82
steam 12
wheels, trailer 138
whistle 162
keeping warm 72
safety 106
winch line 164
Windermere kettle 67
windlass, Spanish 130
wood fuel 10
woodscrews, lubrication 165
work hardening, pipes 39

The Steam Boat Association of Great Britain

exists:

> *To foster and encourage steam boating and the building, development, preservation and restoration of steam boats and steam machinery, by all possible means; to stimulate public interest in steam boats and steam boating; to promote high standards of workmanship, safety and seamanship.*

Among the activities of the SBA are the organisation of rallies, the publication of a quarterly magazine, 'The FUNNEL' and the establishment and administration of standards for construction, maintenance and operation of steam boats.

Membership currently stands at around 1100 in the UK and overseas, and is open to all, whether steam boat owners or not. Enquiries regarding the Association should be addressed to the Honourary Secretary:

or visit the web site at:

http://www.steamboat.org.uk

Also published by CALVERT TECHNICAL PRESS:

STEAM ENGINE PRINCIPLES: Their Application on a Small Scale

by NG Calvert; paperback, 130 pages;
ISBN 0 9513620 1 1; £6.00

A technically sound but accessible introduction to the theory and practise of small scale steam plant. Ideal for the model engineer or preservationist.

STEAM TABLES and Other Data for Steam Enthusiasts

Paperback; 14 pages;
ISBN 0 9513620 2 X; £0.75

Steam tables covering the range of temperature and pressure appropriate to model engineering and small scale plant, in both SI and traditional units. Other data and conversion factors.

Terms: Cash with order. Post and packing 15% UK, 25% overseas surface, 50% overseas airmail (minimum £0.50). Overseas orders over £7.00: we can accept VISA/MasterCard. See our web site:

http://www.ctpress.[illegible]co.uk

for further details and order form.

CALVERT TECHNICAL PRESS, [illegible]t,
S[illegible]Telephone: [illegible]1